ENDGAME CHALLENGE!

by

Senior Master John Hall

Hays Publishing

Author: John Hall

Editor: Lou Hays

Book Design and Typeset: Lou Hays

Computer file creation: John Hall

Proofreaders: David Sewell, John Hall, Jude Acers

PRINTED IN THE UNITED STATES OF AMERICA

Second printing June, 1998

Hays Publishing

P.O. Box 777

Park Hill, Oklahoma 74451

ISBN 1-880673-98-3

TABLE OF CONTENTS

EXPLANATION OF SYMBOLS

(Below diagram)	**W**	+ -	White To Play and Win
(Below diagram)	**W**	=	White To Play and Draw
(Below diagram)	**W**	- +	White To Play, Black Wins
(Below diagram)	**B**	- +	Black To Play and Win
(Below diagram)	**B**	=	Black To Play and Draw
(Below diagram)	**B**	+ -	Black To Play, White Wins

!	Strong Move
!!	Very Strong Move
?	Weak Move
??	Blunder
+	Check
#	Checkmate

TAKE THE BOREDOM OUT
OF ENDGAME STUDY!

One of the most difficult projects for the average chessplayer is the act of sitting down to study endgames. Many players simply never get around to it, while others take an occasional stab at the subject only to give up before they've learned anything useful. The reason is not hard to find: most of us feel that learning endings is a dry and boring process.

Not so with *Endgame Challenge!* This book offers a fun and dynamic approach to rapid improvement in endgame skill. Rather than pore endlessly over rules and techniques in some dusty 500-page manual, you can now take an active part in your endgame education! Here's a sample of how to get the most out of this book:

First, turn to any page with diagrams and follow these steps–

1) Pick a diagram to solve and cover the **hint** on the right side of the page. Next try to find the right idea for the win (or draw), spending no more than five to ten minutes.

2) If you are stumped, uncover the **hint** to the right of the diagram. This will tell you the difficulty of the example and offer a bit of useful advice.

3) If after seeing the **hint** you still cannot find the answer within another ten minutes, look it up at the end of the chapter and *try to remember the winning or drawing idea!*

Give yourself **3** points for every ending you solve marked *difficult,* **2** points for those marked *moderate,* and **1** point for the *easy* ones. That way you will be able to measure your progress when you go through the book a second time. Unlike middlegame combinations, there is often more than one route to winning or drawing endings. Award yourself the point(s) if you find the right idea and the book line or a line equally as effective. You will find that many of the easier examples can be solved without setting up a chessboard, but plan to use your equipment when you tackle the more difficult endings. It is important to work on a few diagrams every day. This will benefit you more than trying to go through the whole book one Saturday afternoon!

Remember, repetition is a key to learning endings—but so is having fun! *Endgame Challenge!* offers an enjoyable method of improving your endgame skill. By the time you have been through all the examples, you will know more about endings than most tournament players and you will have greatly increased the number of positions you *fully* understand—the ultimate key to improving at chess.

THE BASICS

We begin with the basic checkmates along with examples of pieces in direct combat with each other with no pawns on the board. One must be familiar with the ideas behind these endings in order to know whether he can "trade down" to a known winning or drawing position. Be not deceived! Many of these endings are tricky, such as Queen vs Rook, or King, Bishop and Knight vs King.

Take the time to go over the basic mates until you fully understand them and know you can play them successfully in a tournament game.

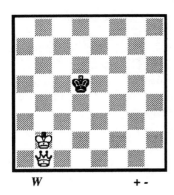

W + -

No.1
HINT: Checkmate with King + Queen vs King. The enemy King must be forced to the edge of the board.

EASY

W + -

No.2
HINT: Checkmate with King + Rook vs King. The enemy King must be forced to the edge of the board.

EASY

B + -

No.3
HINT: Checkmate with King and two Bishops vs King. The enemy King must be forced into a corner.

MODERATE

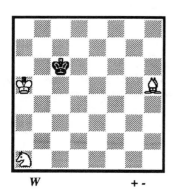

W   + -

No.4

HINT: The enemy King must be driven to edge of the board, then into a corner of the same color as the Bishop.

DIFFICULT

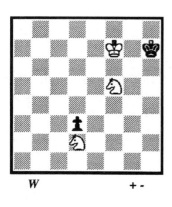

W   + -

No.5

HINT: Two Knights cannot mate vs lone King–with an extra pawn the weaker side can (in some positions) be forced into mate because tempo moves with the pawn disallow stalemate defenses.

MODERATE

B   + -

No.6

HINT: Utilizing *zugzwang* (the unwanted compulsion to move) and mating threats to force the win.

MODERATE

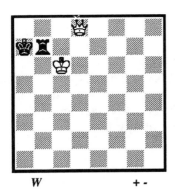

W + -

No.7
HINT: White to move wants to "lose" a move in order to impose *zugzwang*.

MODERATE

W + -

No.8
HINT: King and Queen "crowd" enemy forces with threats to mate or win the Rook.

MODERATE

B =

No.9
HINT: Rook can sometimes draw against Queen by use of perpetual check and/or stalemate tactics.

MODERATE

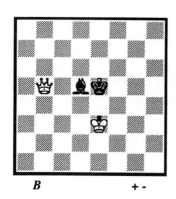

B   + -

No. 10

HINT: King and Queen penetrate on squares of opposite color to Bishop, driving enemy King to edge of board.

EASY

W   + -

No. 11

HINT: King and Queen encroach on King and Knight to force mate.

EASY

B   =

No. 12

HINT: This ending is normally drawn, but the defender must remain alert!

MODERATE

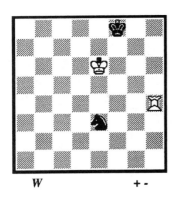

W   + -

No.13

HINT: When defender's King and Knight are separated, the win is often possible by threats to win the Knight or checkmate.

MODERATE

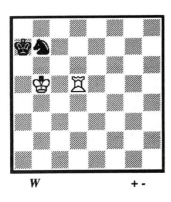

W   + -

No.14

HINT: Even if defender's King and Knight are close together, they can often be tactically vulnerable.

EASY

W   =

No.15

HINT: Rook vs Bishop is usually a draw if the defending King can get to corner of opposite color to Bishop (Except for some tactical quirks.)

EASY

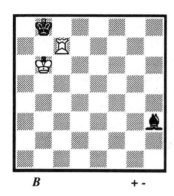

B   **+ -**

No.16
HINT: With the defender's King in the "wrong" corner (i.e., the same color as the Bishop.) the position is lost.

EASY

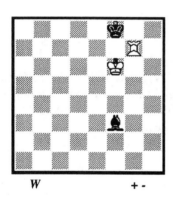

W   **+ -**

No.17
HINT: White wins by combining threats to the Bishop with mating threats.

DIFFICULT

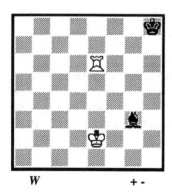

W   **+ -**

No.18
HINT: The Bishop can be snared.

EASY

SOLUTIONS FOR EXAMPLES 1-18

1) **1.Kc3 Ke5 2.Qg6** (Cutting down the Black King's flight squares.) **Kf4 3.Kd4 Kf3 4.Qg5 Kf2 5.Qg4** (Forcing the King to the edge of the board.) **Ke1 6.Qg2 Kd1 7.Kd3 Kc1 8.Qc2#**. NOTE: this is, of course not the only solution, just demonstration of basic ideas.

2) **1.Kc2 Ke4 2.Kc3 Ke5 3.Kc4 Ke4** (With Kings "face-to-face" it's time to check with the Rook.) **4.Re1+ Kf5 5.Kd4 Kf4 6.Rf1+ Kg5 7.Ke4 Kg6 8.Ke5 Kg5 9.Rg1+ Kh4 10.Kf5 Kh3 11.Kf4 Kh2 12.Rg3 Kh1 13.Kf3 Kh2 14.Kf2 Kh1 15.Rh3#**. NOTE: As in example No.1, there is more than one solution to this problem.

3) **1...Kf3 2 Bd3** (The Bishops gradually "crowd" the King to the desired corner.) **2...Kf4 3.Be4 Kg5 4.Ke5 Kg4 5.Bf2 Kg5 6.Bf5 Kh6 7.Kf6 Kh5 8.Be6 Kh6 9.Bg4 Kh7 10.Kf7 Kh6 11.Be3+ Kh7 12.Bf5+ Kh8 13.Bd4#** NOTE: as in previous examples, other solutions are possible.

4) **1.Nb3** (White's pieces must cooperate like parts in a well-oiled machine. This is easier said than done, since up to 35 moves may be required.) **Kd6 2.Kb5 Kd5 3.Bf7+ Ke5** (3...Kd6 4.Bc4 Ke5 5.Kc5 Ke4 6. Kd6 Kf5 7.Bd3+ Kf6 8.Nd2 Kf7 9.Nc4 Kf6 10.Ne5 Kg7 11.Ke7 Kh8 12.Kf6 Kg8 13.Nf7 transposes into the position (with White to move) after Black's 13th move in our main line.) **4.Kc5 Kf6 5.Bc4 Ke5 6.Nd2 Kf4 7.Kd6 Kf5 8.Bd3+ Kf6 9.Nf3 Kf7 10.Ke5 Kg7** (10...Ke7 11.Bc4.) **11.Ng5 Kg8 12.Kf6 Kf8 13.Nf7 Kg8** (The enemy King has "run" to the corner of opposite color to the Bishop. Now White's task is to chase the King to the "right" corner.) **14.Bf5 Kf8 15.Bh7 Ke8 16.Ne5 Kd8 17.Ke6** (Or 17.Be6.) **Kc7 18.Nd7 Kb7 19.Bd3 Kc6 20.Ba6 Kc7 21.Bb5 Kd8 22.Nb6 Kc7 23.Nd5+ Kd8 24.Kd6 Kc8 25.Ke7 Kb7 26.Kd7 Kb8 27.Ba6 Ka7 28.Bc8 Kb8 29.Ne7 Ka7 30.Kc7 Ka8 31.Bb7+** (Not 31.Nc6?? which stalemates.) **Ka7 32.Nc6# or 32.Nc8#**.

5) **1.Ne4 d2** (1...Kh8 2.Nf6 d2 transposes.) **2.Nf6+ Kh8 3.Ne7 d1=Q** (Note: It would be stalemate if Black didn't have the pawn.) **4.Ng6#**.

6) We list below Black's main possibilities:
   a) 1...Rb1 2.Qd4+ Kb8 3.Qh8+ Ka7 4.Qh7+ wins the Rook.
   b) 1...Rb3 2.Qd4+ Kb8 3.Qf4+ Ka7 4.Qa4+ wins the Rook.
   c) 1...Rf7 2.Qd4+ Kb8 3.Qb2+ Ka8 (3...Kc8 4.Qh8+.) 4.Qa2+ wins the Rook..
   d) 1...Rh7 2.Qd4+ Kb8 3.Qe5+ Ka7 4.Qa1+ Kb8 5.Qb1+ wins the Rook.
   e) 1...Rb4 2.Qa5+ (Or 2.Qe7+.) wins the Rook.

f) 1...Rg7 2.Qd4+ wins the Rook.

g) 1...Rb2 2.Qd4+ wins the Rook.

h) 1...Ka6 allows the winning pin 2.Qc8.

7) 1.Qd4+ (White must be alert to stalemate defenses,e.g., 1.Qc8 Rb6+ 2.Kc7?? Rc6+! since 3.Kxc6 is stalemate.) **1...Kb8** (Or 1...Ka8 2.Qh8+ Ka7 [2...Rb8 allows 3.Qa1#] 3.Qd8 transposing into our main line.) **2.Qh8+ Ka7 3.Qd8** and we arrive at example No.6 – having "lost" a move by the initial Queen maneuver.

8) 1.Qc6+ Kd8 2.Qa8+ (Or 2.Kd6?? allowing 2...Re6+! 3.Kxe6 with stalemate.) **Kc7 3.Qf8** and now:

a) 3...Re2 4.Qg7+ Kd8 5.Qg5+ Kc7 6.Qf4+ Kd8 7.Kd6 Ke8 (7...Kc8 8.Qc4+.) 8.Qh6! Kd8 (8...Kf7 9.Qh5+.) 9.Qf8+ Re8 10.Qf7 and mate can't be stopped.

b) 3...Re3 4.Qf4+ wins the Rook.

c) 3...Re1 4.Qf4+ Kd7 5.Qg4+ Ke8 6.Kd6 wins, as in a.)

d) 3...Rd7+ 4.Kc5 Kb7 (4...Rd8 5.Qf4+ Kd7 6.Qf7+ Kc8 7.Kc6 and mate follows.) 5.Qe8 Rc7+ 6.Kb5 Ka7 7.Qe4 Rb7+ 8.Kc6 Kb8 9.Qe8+ Ka7 10.Qd8 transposing into problem No.6.

e) 3...Kd7 4.Qb8 Rf7 (If 4...Re3 5.Qa7+, or 4...Re2 5.Qb5+ wins; also on 4...Re1 5.Qb5+ Kc8 6.Qc4+ Kd7 7.Qa4+ Kc8 8.Kd6! [threatening 9.Qa8#] and Black gets mated or loses the Rook.) 5.Qb7+ Ke8 6.Qc8+ Ke7 7.Ke5 Rg7 (Or 7... Rf3 8.Qb7+; 7...Rf1 8.Qc5+ Kd8 9.Qa5+ Ke7 10.Qb4+ Kd8 11.Ke6! wins as in a) and c); 7...Rf2 8.Qc5+.) 8.Qc7+ Kf8 9.Qd8+ Kf7 10.Kf5 Rh7 11.Qd7+ Kg8 12.Qe8+ Kg7 13.Kg5 Rh8 14.Qe7+ Kg8 15.Kg6 and mate follows.

9) 1...Rg7+ 2.Kf5 (On 2. Kf6 Black has the resource 2...Rg6+! since 3.Kxg6 is stalemate.) **Rf7+ 3.Kg6** (Not 3.Ke5/e4 as 3...Re7 draws.) **Rg7+ 4.Kh6 Rh7+** (Again the stalemate motif. White must acquiesce to a draw, since Black simply continues checking on the g- and h-files; White's King can never cross the e-file since then ...Re7 draws.)

10) 1...Kd6 2.Kd4 Be6 3.Qb6+ Ke7 4.Ke5 Bf7 5.Qd6+ Ke8 6.Kf6 and 7.Qe7# cannot be stopped.

11) 1.Qb6 Ne6 2.Kd5 Nc7+ 3.Ke5 Ne8 4.Qe6+ Kd8 5.Qf7 Nc7 6.Kd6 Nb5+ 7.Kc5 Nc7 8.Kc6 and mate next.

12) 1...Nh7+ (Not 1...Kh8 2.Re8 Kg8 3.Ra8 and the Knight is lost.) **2.Kg6 Nf8+ 3.Kh6 Kh8 4.Rf7 Kg8** (Not 4...Ne6 5.Rf6 winning.) **5.Rg7+ Kh8**

6.Rg1 Nd7! (Forced, but quite adequate; 6...Nh7 loses to 7.Kg6 Kg8 [7...Nf8+ 8.Kf7 Nh7 9.Rg8#, or 8...Nd7 9.Rh1#.] 8.Rg2 Nf8+ 9.Kf6+ Kh8 10.Kf7, etc; or if 6...Ne6 then 7.Kg6 Nf8+ 8.Kf7 winning.) **7.Kg6 Kg8 8.Rg2** (On 8.Rd1 Nf8+ holds the draw.) **8...Kf8** and White can't make any progress–it's a draw. Black must maintain "contact" between King and Knight, otherwise White will "surround" the Knight and win it or force checkmate.

13) 1.Re4 Nd1 (If 1...Ng2 2.Kf6 Kg8 3.Kg5 followed by 4.Re2 wins the Knight. Or 1...Nc2 2.Kd5 Na3 3.Kc5 Nb1 4.Kb4 Nd2 5.Rf4+ Ke7 6.Kc3 Nb1+ 7.Kb2 Nd2 8.Kc2 trapping the Knight.) **2.Rf4+ Kg7 3.Rf3 Kg6 4.Ke5 Kg5 5.Kd4 Kg4 6.Rf1 Nb2 7.Rb1 Na4 8.Rb4** winning the Knight.

14) 1.Rd7 Kb8 2.Kb6 Ka8 (Since 3.Rxb7?? is stalemate.) **3.Rg7 Nd8 4.Rg8** wins the Knight and mates next move.

15) If **1.Ra8+** then simply **1...Bg8** and White can make no progress because stalemate occurs after 2.Kg6 or any Rook move on the 8th rank.

16) 1...Bg4 2.Rg7 Be6 3.Re7 Bg4 4.Re8+ (Forcing the Bishop into a fatal pin.) **Bc8 5.Rh8 Ka8 6.Rxc8#.**

17) 1.Rg3 Be4 (On 1...Bb7 2.Rb3; or 1...Ba8 2.Rb3 and the threat of Rb8+ wins in both cases. Or if 1...Bc6 then 2.Rc3 Bd7 3.Rb3 Ke8 [3...Kg8 4.Rb8+ Kh7 5.Rb7] 4.Rb8+ wins.) **2.Re3 Bg2** (2...Bh7 is met by 3.Rb3! since 3...Kg8 allows 4.Rb8#, and 3...Ke8 4.Rb8+ Kd7 5. Rb7+ wins the Bishop.) **3.Re2 Bf3 4.Rf2 Bc6** (Or 4...Be4 5.Ke5+ while 4...Bg4 loses to 5.Kg5+.) **5.Rc2 Bd7 6.Rb2 Bc6 7.Rb8+ Be8 8.Ra8** (Achieving *zugzwang*) **Kg8 9.Rxe8+** winning.

18) 1.Kf3! wins:
   a) 1...Bb8 2.Re8+ and 3.Rxb8.
   b) 1...Bc7 2.Re8+ King moves and 3.Re7+ followed by 4.Rxc7.
   c) 1...Bh4 (Or 1...Bh2) 2.Rh6+ and 3.Rxh4 (Or 3.Rxh2).

KING AND PAWN ENDINGS

King and pawn endings are the most essential type of ending. This is because almost every other type of ending can simplify down to the King and pawn variety.

In this chapter we cover a wide range of methods and techniques used to win (or draw) such endings. One important technique is use of the "opposition" –which enables the player possessing it to drive the opponent's King from control of vital squares. Another technique is triangulation, which is a means of obtaining the opposition by maneuvering in a triangle of squares. The "distant" opposition is often an important resource (see example No.27.) You will be shown how to obtain and utilize passed pawns–including the so-called "outside passer" and "protected passer."

In various configurations of Kings and pawns we illustrate a multitude of technical methods leading to the win and draw. The stalemate defense is often the means of holding an otherwise lost position–in some of these problems it will arise most unexpectedly with considerable aesthetic appeal. In many cases where one side is a pawn down there are critical drawing resources–will you be able to find them?

Study of all the examples which follow will greatly enhance your understanding of how to successfully negotiate the many twists and turns often seen (even in seemingly simple-looking positions) in King and pawn endings.

Although most of the following examples are grouped within common themes, it must be kept in mind that there is quite often more than one theme or technique at work in each problem.

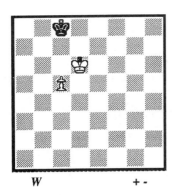

W + -

No.19
HINT: Introducing the concept of opposition, in this case in order to Queen a pawn.

EASY

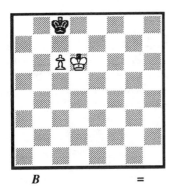

B =

No.20
HINT: Using opposition to prevent the opponent from Queening a pawn.

EASY

B + -

No.21
HINT: White has the opposition and thus can promote the pawn.

EASY

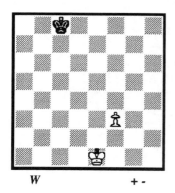

W   + -

No.22
HINT: Maneuvering to gain opposition and Queen a pawn.

MODERATE

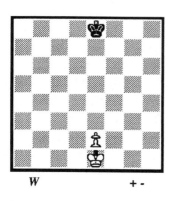

W   + -

No.23
HINT: Black has the opposition initially, but the "reserve" move of White's pawn allows White to gain the opposition.

EASY

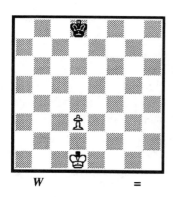

W   =

No.24
HINT: Black has the opposition, but White cannot obtain it since the d-pawn has no "reserve" moves.

EASY

W =

No.25
HINT: White draws by sacrificing a pawn to gain the opposition.

MODERATE

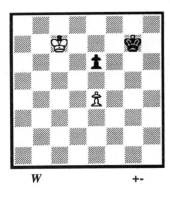

W +-

No.26
HINT: Sometimes having the opposition doesn't work as the defender runs out of squares to fall back upon. (Because the defender's King is on the edge of the board.)

EASY

W =

No.27
HINT: A pawn sacrifice gains the "distant" opposition.

DIFFICULT

No.28

HINT: Black draws by a pawn sac to gain the opposition or reach a classic "must know" drawn position.

MODERATE

No.29

HINT: Black draws by a pawn sacrifice to gain the opposition.

MODERATE

No.30

HINT: Even though White has the move, Black can draw by sacrificing his pawn.

MODERATE

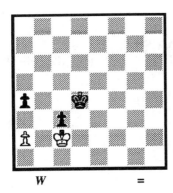

W =

No.31
HINT: White must not take the opposition, since he has an unfortunate "reserve" tempo move with the a-pawn.

MODERATE

W =

No.32
HINT: White draws by a pawn sacrifice to retain the opposition.

MODERATE

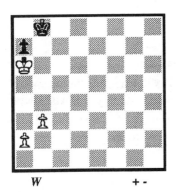

W + -

No.33
HINT: White chooses the correct initial pawn moves to eventually force the Black King away to gain the opposition and promote a pawn.

MODERATE

W   + -

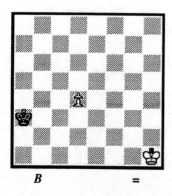

B   =

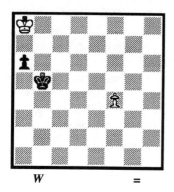

W   =

No.34
HINT: Obtaining the "distant" opposition.

MODERATE

No.35
HINT: Introducing the concept of the "square" of a passed pawn. The weaker side's King can catch an enemy passer only if it can enter the "square" of the pawn (And the other side's King cannot come up to help it's passer.) The "square" of the passer is formed by a line extending from the passer to it's Queening square and a line extending laterally the same number of squares (or less, but never more) toward the side of the board.

EASY

No.36
HINT: Entering the square of the enemy passed pawn with threats to promote one's own passed pawn.

MODERATE

W =

No.37

HINT: White draws by continuing to threaten to enter the "square" of the enemy passer.

MODERATE

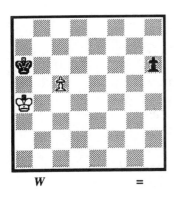

W =

No.38

HINT: White draws by combining threats to Queen his own pawn with threats to enter the "square" of the enemy passer.

MODERATE

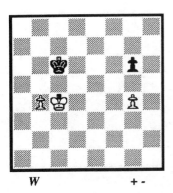

W + -

No.39

HINT: An "outside" passer is a passed pawn which causes the opponent's King to be diverted from defending against crucial events on another sector of the board. Usually both Kings are on one flank, while the "outside" passer is on the opposite flank. In this case the "outside" passer is on the same side as both Kings, but it still provides the intended diversionary effect.

EASY

W   =

No.40
HINT: Sometimes an "outside" passer doesn't win if the defender's King can return to the critical area in time.

EASY

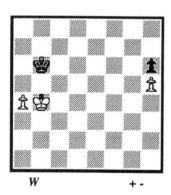

W   + -

No.41
HINT: White wins here because his King can "head-off" the Black King's efforts to get to h8, with the typical drawing position–see example No.40.

EASY

B   - +

No.42
HINT: Black's better King position is turned to account.

MODERATE

W   +-

No.43
HINT: The outside" passer wins.

EASY

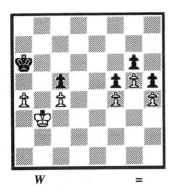

W   =

No.44
HINT: Even with an extra "outside" passer, White can't win because his King can't penetrate into Black's position.

EASY

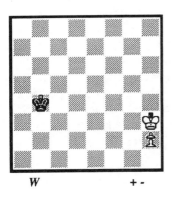

W   + -

No.45
HINT: White wins because with the move his King gets to g7– which allows the h-pawn to promote.

MODERATE

B =

No.46
HINT: With the move Black can draw by rushing his King toward f8 to blockade White's attempts to Queen the h-pawn.

MODERATE

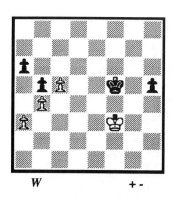

W + -

No.47
HINT: An example of the protected passed pawn winning against an outside passed pawn.

MODERATE

W =

No.48
HINT: In some (rather rare) positions, a protected passer can't win against a single pawn–here it's because of stalemate.

MODERATE

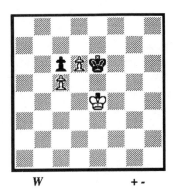

W + -

No.49
HINT: White sacrifices a pawn to "outflank" the enemy King and gain the opposition.

MODERATE

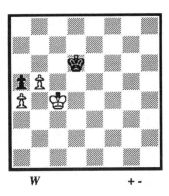

W + -

No.50
HINT: White must "outflank" the enemy King. The sacrifice of the b-pawn doesn't work because White is left with an a-pawn, drawing.

MODERATE

W =

No.51
HINT: Black draws due to the possibilities of a drawn a-pawn ending and stalemate.

MODERATE

B   + -

No.52

HINT: As we've seen before (example No.51), even an extra protected passed pawn may not win in some positions. Here White can win only if he can get his King off of the back rank.

MODERATE

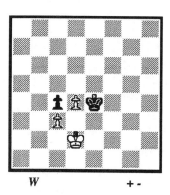

W   + -

No.53

HINT: Sometimes, in order to win, it is necessary to "lose a move" from the starting position,i.e. White wants the diagramed position with Black to move. In order to do this the White King circulates upon three adjacent squares, eventually giving us the original position with Black to move. This technique is called "triangulation".

DIFFICULT

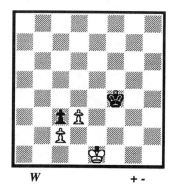

W   + -

No.54

HINT: With the move, White wins by maneuvering his King.

EASY

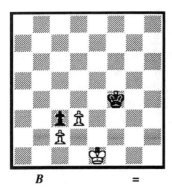

B =

No.55
HINT: With the move, Black draws by restricting the movements of the White King.

MODERATE

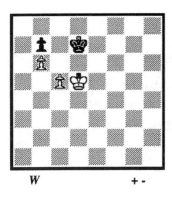

W + -

No.56
HINT: Using triangulation to force the win.

MODERATE

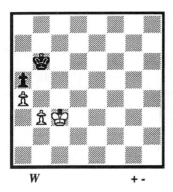

W + -

No.57
HINT: White wins by gaining the opposition to win the a-pawn.

EASY

B =

No.58
HINT: Black can draw because the White King has insufficient maneuvering space to "outflank" the Black King.

MODERATE

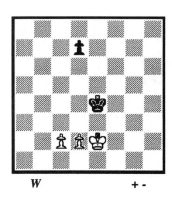

W + -

No.59
HINT: White must carefully advance his King and pawns to avoid drawing tricks.

MODERATE

W + -

No.60
HINT: White "outflanks" the Black King to win the b-pawn.

EASY

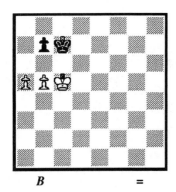

B   =

No.61
HINT: Black to move draws by a tactical trick to gain the opposition.

MODERATE

W   =

No.62
HINT: White can't win because of a stalemate defense.

MODERATE

W   =

No.63
HINT: Black's "fortress-like" position can't be penetrated, mainly because of stalemate possibilities.

EASY

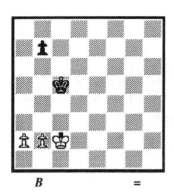

B   =

No.64
HINT: Black draws by maintaining the opposition (including the "distant" opposition.)

DIFFICULT

B   + -

No.65
HINT: With the move, Black loses since he can't hold the opposition.

MODERATE

B   =

No.66
Example No.65 moved down one rank, which enables Black to draw.

MODERATE

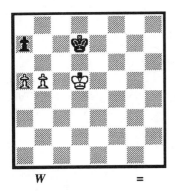

W   =

No.67
HINT: Black draws by stalemate defenses.

MODERATE

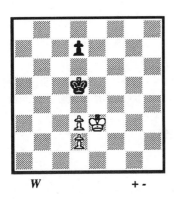

W   + -

No.68
HINT: When White's doubled pawns are on the same file as Black's pawn, it is normally a win.

MODERATE

B   =

No.69
HINT: Black draws by a timely counterattack against White's pawns.

MODERATE

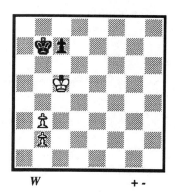

W   + -

No.70
HINT: White wins because Black's King can't counterattack the White pawns as in example No.69.

MODERATE

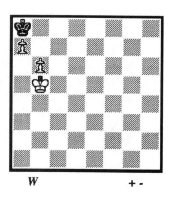

W   + -

No.71
HINT: White sacrifices the a-pawn to avoid Black's stalemate defense.

EASY

W   =

No.72
HINT: White draws by a subtle stalemate resource.

DIFFICULT

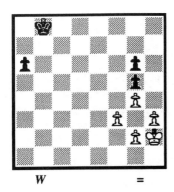

W =

No.73
HINT: White draws by threats to obtain a passer as well as using a problem-like stalemate defense.

DIFFICULT

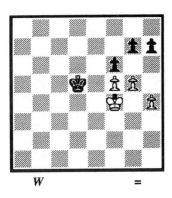

W =

No.74
HINT: This position comes from a Chigorin-Tarrasch game in which White resigned. However there is a hidden stalemate defense which would have drawn.

DIFFICULT

W + -

No.75
HINT: White creates a winning passer with a well-known tactical trick.

EASY

W   + -

No.76
HINT: Clever tactics allow White to Queen a pawn.

MODERATE

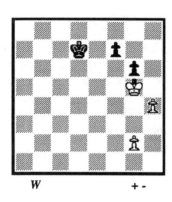

W   + -

No.77
HINT: White must not try to create a passer right away, but instead restrict the Black King.

DIFFICULT

B   - +

No.78
HINT: Black's superior space control and aggressive King position allow the win.

DIFFICULT

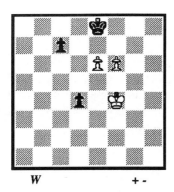

W   + -

No.79

HINT: The advanced connected passers are put into action after some preliminary "triangulation" to win a tempo.

DIFFICULT

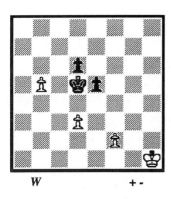

W   + -

No.80

HINT: White sacrifices a pawn, which slows down Black's intentions of capturing White's b-pawn, the time gained in the process allows White to win.

DIFFICULT

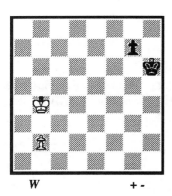

W   + -

No.81

HINT: White's King must maneuver precisely to advance his pawn while hindering Black's passer.

DIFFICULT

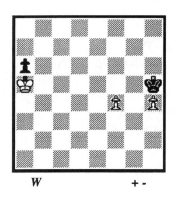

W + -

No.82
HINT: Utilization of the fact that two passers separated by one file can "defend" each other indirectly.

MODERATE

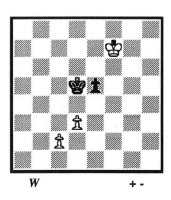

W + -

No.83
HINT: The White King must pick the right path to help a pawn Queen.

MODERATE

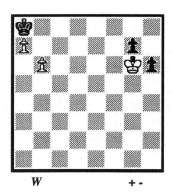

W + -

No.84
HINT: The tempo balance plus a tactical twist equals a win.

MODERATE

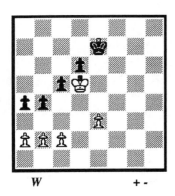

No.85

HINT: White's superior King position proves decisive after some preliminary pawn play.

MODERATE

W   + -

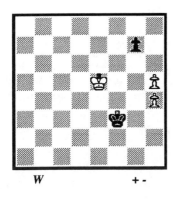

No.86

HINT: White wins with a well-timed pawn sacrifice.

MODERATE

W   + -

No.87

HINT: White must advance his pawns accurately to secure the win.

DIFFICULT

W   + -

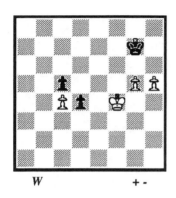

W   + -

No.88
HINT: White's advanced connected passers supported by the
King outweigh the protected passer
at d4.

MODERATE

SOLUTIONS FOR EXAMPLES 19-88

19) 1.Kc6 (Forcing Black's King out of the way of the c-pawn's path to c8.)
1...Kb8 (1...Kd8 2.Kb7 and c6, c7, and c8=Q) **2.Kd7 Kb7 3.c6+ Kb8 4.c7+**
and **5.c8=Q** wins. NOTE: With White having the initial move he places his
King directly in "opposition" to Black's Kc8. Also note that an odd number
of squares between the Kings in such cases (Here one square.) constitutes
the opposition if the opponent's King has the move.

20) 1...Kd8 (Gaining the opposition.) **2.c7+** (2.Kc5 makes no progress
against 2...Kc7) **2...Kc8 3.Kc6** (Otherwise the pawn is lost.) and it's a draw
by stalemate.

21) 1...Kb5 2.Kd4 Kc6 3.Kc4 (White maintains the opposition to drive
Black's King away from critical squares.) **3...Kb6 4.Kd5 Kc7 5.Kc5 Kd7
6.Kb6 Kc8** (6...Kd6 7.c4 Kd7 8.c5 Kc8 9.Kc6 wins.) **7.Kc6 Kd8 8.c4 Kc8
9.c5 Kd8 10.Kb7** and with c6, c7, and c8 controlled, the c-pawn will Queen
in three moves.

22) 1.Kf2 Kd7 2.Kg3 Ke6 3.Kg4 Kf6 (Or 3...Ke5 4.Kg5.) **4.Kf4** (Gaining
the opposition.) **4...Ke6 5.Kg5 Kf7 6.Kf5 Ke8 7.Kf6 Kf8 8.f4 Ke8 9.Kg7**
and with f6, f7, and f8 under control, the pawn Queens in four moves.

23) 1.Kd2 Kd8 2.Ke3 Ke7 3.Ke4 Ke6 4.e3! (The "reserve" move of this
pawn gains the opposition.) **4...Kd6 5.Kf5 Ke7 6.Ke5** and the pawn will
promote by force–see example No.19.

24) 1.Kd2 Kd7 2.Ke3 Ke7 3.Kd4 Kd6 4.Ke4 Ke6 and White is getting nowhere since Black can hold the opposition.

25) 1.f4! (Not 1.Kd2 f4! 2.Ke2 Kc3 3.Ke1 Kd3 4.Kf2 Kd2 5.Kf1 Ke3 6.Kg2 Ke2 winning the pawn.) **1...Ke4 2.Ke1 Ke3** (On 2...Kxf4 then 3.Kf2 gains the opposition and draws.) **3.Kf1 Kf3 4.Ke1 Kxf4 5.Kf2** and it's a draw since White has gained the opposition.

26) 1.e5! (White will win the e6 pawn and Black's opposition will not draw as he will run out of squares against the edge of the board.) **1...Kf8 2.Kd7 Kf7 3.Kd6 Kf8 4.Kxe6 Ke8 5.Kf6** (Or 5.Kd6 Kd8 6.e6.) **5...Kf8** (5...Kd8 6.Kf7) **6.e6 Ke8 7.e7 Kd7 8.Kf7** and Queens.

27) 1.e5!! (Sacrificing the pawn to obtain the "distant" opposition– opposition with not just one, but three or five squares between the Kings.) **1...dxe5 2.Kc1!** (Keeping an odd number of squares between the Kings; in this case since it's more than one square between the Kings, it's called the "distant" opposition.) **2...Kd5** (2...Kd4 3.Kd2) **3.Kd1** (Still keeping an odd number of squares between the Kings.) **3...Kd4 4.Kd2 Ke4 5.Ke2** and it's an elementary draw.

28) 1...a5! (Now if 2.bxa5 then the "must know" draw [referring to positions with only an a- or h-pawn remaining] arises, since the Black King can reach a8, blocking the a-pawn's path toward Queening. For example: 2.bxa5 Ka8 3.Kb6 Kb8 4.a6 Ka8 5.Kc7 Ka7 and wins the pawn, while 5.a7 is stalemate– this stalemate being typical in positions with an a- or h-pawn.) **2.b5 Kb8** (Not 2...a4? since 3.Kc7 a3 4.b6+ Ka6 5.b7 a2 6.b8=Q a1=Q 7.Qa8+ wins Black's Queen) **3.Kc5 Kb7 4.b6 a4 5.Kb4 Kxb6 6.Kxa4** drawn.

29) 1.d4 Ke8 2.Kc7 d5! (Not 2...Ke7 as White wins after 3.d5 Ke8 4.d6 Kf7 5.Kxd7) **3.Kc6 Ke7 4.Kxd5 Kd7** and Black has obtained the opposition, thus drawing.

30) 1.Kc7 Ka8! 2.Kb6 (It looks like a White win, but...) **2...a5!** (Now 3.bxa5 allows Black a standard draw–see example No.28.) **3.b5! Kb8!** (Not 3...a4? 4.Kc7 and White will Queen with check.) **4.Kxa5 Ka7** gaining the opposition and drawing.

31) 1.Kd1! (Taking the opposition here loses because of an [unwanted] "reserve" move of the a-pawn: 1.Kc1? Kd3 2.Kd1 c2+ 3.Kc1 Kc3 4.a3 [it would be stalemate without this pawn move, but now White loses] 4...Kb3 5.Kd2 Kb2 and wins.) **1...Kd3 2.Kc1 c2 3.a3 Kc3** (otherwise the c-pawn falls) and it's stalemate.

32) 1.b4+! cxb4+ (Or 1...Kb6 2.bxc5+ Kxc5 3.Kb3 and White retains the opposition after 3...b4 4.Kb2 Kc4 5.Kc2 with a draw.) **2.Kb3 Ka6 3.Kxb4 Kb6 4.Kb3 Kc5** (4...Ka5 5.Ka3) **5.Kc3** and White retains the opposition with a draw.

33) 1.b4 Ka8 2.b5 Kb8 3.a3! (Saving a "reserve" tempo in order to force Black's King to give way at the proper time.) **3...Ka8 4.a4 Kb8 5.a5 Ka8 6.b6 axb6 7.axb6 Kb8 8.b7 Kc7 9.Ka7** and Queens. NOTE: 3.a4? would destroy the proper tempo balance and allow Black to draw by stalemate in the final position (It would be <u>White</u> to move at the position: White Ka6, pawn b7; Black Kb8.

34) 1.Ke2! (Obtaining the "distant" opposition–see example No.27.) **1...Ke7** (On 1...Kd8 2.Kf3 Ke7 3.Ke3! keeps the "distant" opposition.) **2.Ke3 Ke6 3.Ke4 Kf6 4.Kf4!** (Not 4.Kd5? Kf5 5.Kc5 Kg4 6.Kxb5 Kxh4 7.Kc5 Kg4 and Black Queens just after White with a draw.) **4...Kg6 5.Ke5 Kh6 6.Kf6 Kh7 7.Kg5 Kg7 8.Kxh5 Kh7 9.Kg5** and White wins easily by sacrificing the h-pawn to divert the Black King; then the White King rushes to the Queenside to win the b-pawn, after which the b-pawn Queens before the Black King can return to defend.

35) 1...Kb4 (Entering the "square" of the passer. Not 1...Ka4? [which also enters the "square" but also allows the passer's King to come up to its defense] 2.Kg2 Kb5 3.Kf3 Kc4 4.Ke4 and White wins.) **2.d5 Kc5** and the pawn is captured.

36) 1.Kb7 a5 2.Kc7! (threatening to successfully advance the f-pawn) **2...Kc5** (2...a4 3.f5 a3 4.f6 a2 5.f7 and both sides Queen with a draw) **3.Kd7 Kd5 4.Ke7 Ke4 5.Ke6 Kxf4 6.Kd5!** and by entering the "square" of the enemy passer, White draws.

37) 1.Kg7 h5 2.Kf6 h4 3.Ke5 h3 (3...Kb6 4.Kf4 enters the "square", drawing) **4.Kd6! h2 5.c7 Kb7 6.Kd7 h1=Q 7.c8=Q+** with a draw.

38) 1.c6! h5 (1...Kb6 2.Kb4 will transpose into our main line.) **2.Kb4! Kb6** (On 2...h4 3.Kc5! h3 4.Kd6 and White Queens his passer in the nick of time.) **3.Kc4 h4** (On 3...Kxc6 4.Kd4 enters the "square" of the h-pawn, drawing.) **4.Kd5 h3** (Or 4...Kc7 5.Ke4, again entering the "square.") **5.Kd6 h2 6.c7 Kb7 7.Kd7 h1=Q 8.c8=Q+** with a draw.

39) 1.b5+ Kb6 2.Kd5 Kxb5 3.Ke6 Kc5 4.Kf6 Kd5 5.Kxg6 Ke6 6.g5 Ke7 7.Kh7 and White Queens by force in three moves.

40) 1.Kc4 Ka5 2.Kd5 Kxa4 3.Ke5 Kb5 4.Kf5 Kc6 5.Kg5 Kd7 6.Kxh5 Ke8 7.Kg6 Kf8 8.h5 (8.Kh7 Kf7 allows Black to draw since the White King is confined to the h-file, thus perpetually blocking his own pawn. For example, 9.Kh6 Kf6 10.Kh7 Kf7,etc.) **8...Kg8** and the Black King gets to h8 with a sure draw—see example No.28.

41) 1.Kc4 Ka5 2.Kd5 Kxa4 3.Ke6 Kb5 4.Kf6 Kc6 5.Kg6 Kd7 6.Kxh6 Ke8 (Trying to reach f8–as in example No.40.) **7.Kg7** stopping 7...Kf8 and assuring the Queening of the h-pawn.

42) 1...Kb4 2.Kc2 Ka3 3.Kb1 a5 4.Ka1 a4 5.bxa4 Kxa4 6.Kb1 (6.Kb2 b4 7.Ka1 Ka3 8.Kb1 b3 9.axb3 Kxb3 wins as in main line.) **6...Ka3 7.Ka1 b4 8.Kb1 b3 9.axb3 Kxb3 10.Kc1 Kc3 11.Kd1 Kd3 12.Ke1 Ke3 13.Kf1 Kf3 14.Kg1 Kxg3** and it's an easy win for Black.

43) 1.Kc4 Ka5 2.Kd5 Kxa4 3.Ke6 Kb4 4.Kf6 and White massacres Black's pawns for an easy win.

44) 1.Kc3 Ka5 2.Kb3 (White can't win because his King has no way to enter Black's position to win Black's pawns.) **2...Ka6** (Or 2...Kb6.) and no progress is possible.

45) 1.Kg4 Kc5 2.Kg5 Kd6 3.Kg6 Ke7 4.Kg7! stopping the Black King from reaching f8. If 4.h4? then 4...Kf8 5.h5 Kg8 draws–see example No.28, while if 5.Kh7 Kf7! draws since White's King is hemmed-in, blocking the path of his h-pawn–see No. 40.

46) 1...Kc5 2.Kg4 Kd6 3.Kf5 Ke7 4.Kg6 Kf8 5.Kh7 (Otherwise 5...Kg8 and 6...Kh8 reaches a known draw–see example Nos.40 and 41.) **5...Kf7 6.h4 Kf8 7.h5 Kf7 8.h6 Kf8 9.Kh8 Kf7 10.h7** stalemate, or 10.Kh7 Kf8 with a repetition of moves.

47) 1.Kg3 Ke5 (1...Kg5?? 2.c6.) **2.Kh4 Kd5 3.Kxh5 Kc6 4.Kg5 Kd5 5.Kf5 Kc6 6.Ke6 Kc7 7.Kd5 Kd7 8.c6+ Kc8 9.Kd6 Kd8 10.c7+ Kc8 11.Kc6 a5 12.bxa5 b4 13.a6 b3 14.a7** and mate next.

48) 1.c8=Q+ (Trying to "outflank" the Black King since the direct 1.Ke5 Kc8 2.Ke6 is stalemate.) **1...Kxc8 2.Ke6 Kd8 3.Kd6 Kc8 4.Ke7 Kb8 5.Kd8 Ka8 6.Kc7** (Or 6.Kc8.) results in stalemate–no progress is possible.

49) 1.d7! Kxd7 2.Kf5 (2.Ke5? Ke7 allows Black to have the opposition and thus draw.) **2...Ke7 3.Ke5 Kd7 4.Kf6 Kc8 5.Ke7 Kc7 6.Ke6 Kc8 7.Kd6 Kd8** (7...Kb7 8.Kd7 Kb8 9.Kxc6 Kc8 10.Kd6 Kd8 11.c6 Kc8 12.c7 and 13.Kd7 wins) **8.Kxc6 Kc8 9.Kd6** winning easily as in the previous note.

50) 1.Kd4 (Sacrificing the b-pawn doesn't work: 1.b6 Kc6 2.b7 Kxb7 3.Kb5 Ka8 draws.) **1...Kc7 2.Kd5 Kb6** (2...Kb7 3.Kc5 Ka7 4.Kc6 wins.) **3.Kd6 Kb7 4.Kd7 Kb8** (4...Ka8 5.Kc7 Ka7 6.b6+ wins.) **5.Kc6 Ka7 6.Kc7 Ka8 7.Kb6** winning easily.

51) 1.Kd4 (1.b7 Kxb7 2.Kd5 Ka7 3.Kc6 Ka8 4.Kb6 wins the pawn but the position is drawn—see example No.28.) **1...Kd6 2.Ke4 Kc6 3.Ke5 Kd7 4.Kd5 Kd8 5.Kd6 Kc8 6.Kc6 Kb8 7.b7 Ka7 8.Kc7** stalemate.

52) 1...Kb6 (Trying to keep White's King trapped against the back rank.) **2.Kb8 Kc6 3.Kc8 Kd6 4.Kd8 Ke6 5.Ke8 Kf6** (Or 5...Kd6 6.Kf7 which is similar to our main line.) **6.Kd7 Ke5 7.Kc6 Ke6 8.Kc5 Ke5 9.Kc4** and wins easily.

53) 1.Kd1! (The obvious 1.Ke2 gets nowhere: 1...Kf4 2.d5 [or 2.Kf2 Ke4 3.Kg3 Kd3 4.d5 Kxc3 5.d6 Kb2 6.d7 c3 7.d8=Q c2 soon arriving at a drawn Queen vs Queen ending] 2...Ke5 3.Ke3 Kxd5 4.Kf4 Kc5 5.Ke4 Kb5 6.Kd4 Kb6! 7.Kxc4 Kc6 and Black draws since he retains the opposition.) **1...Kd5 2.Ke2 Ke4 3.Kd2** (Mission accomplished. Now we have the original position with Black to move.) **Kd5 4.Ke3 Ke6 5.Ke4 Kd6 6.d5 Kc5 7.Ke5** and the pawn Queens shortly.

54) 1.Ke2 (Or 1.Kf2.) **1...Kf5 2.Ke3 Ke5 3.d4+ Kd5 4.Kd3** and **5.Kxc3** wins easily. NOTE: With Black to move, it's a draw. See next example.

55) 1...Kf3! (Not 1...Ke3 2.Kd1 Kf3 3.Kc1 Ke3 4.Kb1 Kd4 5.Ka2 Kc5 6.Kb3 Kd4 7.Kb4,etc.) **2.Kd1** (2.Kf1 Ke3 3.Kg2 Kd2! 4.d4 Kxc2 5.d5 Kb2 and Black draws.) **2...Ke3 3.Kc1 Kd4 4.Kb1 Kc5 5.Ka2 Kb4 6.Ka1 Kb5** (Not 6...Ka3? 7.Kb1 Kb4 8.Kc1 Kc5 9.Kd1 Kd4 10.Ke2 Kd5 11.Ke3 winning.) and it's a draw.

56) 1.Ke5! (Not 1.c6+ Kc8! 2.c7 Kd7 and Black draws- see example No.48.) **1...Kc6** (1...Ke7 2.c6! Kd8 3.cxb7 wins.) **2.Kd4 Kd7 3.Kd5** (White has used triangulation to reach the initial position with Black to move. See example No.53, too.) **3...Kc8 4.Kd6 Kd8 5.Ke6 Kc8 6.Ke7 Kb8 7.Kd7 Ka8 8.c6 bxc6 9.Kc7 c5 10.b7+ Ka7 11.b8=Q+** and mate next.

57) 1.Kd4 (Not 1.Kc4? Kc6 and Black gets the opposition with a draw.) **1...Kc6 2.Kc4 Kb6 3.Kd5 Kb7 4.Kc5 Ka6 5.Kc6 Ka7 6.Kb5** with an easy win.

58) 1...Kd6 (Not 1...Kf6? 2.Kc3 Ke6 3.b4 cxb4+ 4.Kxb4 Kd6 5.Kb5 and the c-pawn will Queen–Black can't get the opposition to draw.) **2.Ke4** (Or 2.Kc3 Kc6 3.b4 cxb4+ 4.Kxb4 Kb6 holding the opposition and drawing.) **Ke6 3.Kf4 Kf6 4.Kg4 Ke5** and White is getting nowhere–draw.

59) 1.Kf2 Kf4 2.d3 Ke5 3.Ke3 d5 4.d4+ (Not 4.c3? allowing the drawing trick 4...d4+! 5.cxd4+ Kd5 6.Ke2 Kxd4 and White can't win as Black retains the opposition.) **4...Kf5 5.Kd3 Ke6 6.Kc3 Kd6 7.Kb4 Kc6 8.Ka5** ("Outflanking" the Black King.) **8...Kc7 9.Kb5 Kd6 10.Kb6 Ke7 11.Kc7 Ke6 12.Kc6** winning easily.

60) 1.Kc3 Kd5 2.Kb4 Kc6 3.Ka5 Kc5 4.b4+ Kc4 (4...Kc6 5.Ka6 wins the pawn.) **5.Kb6 Kb3 6.Kxb5 Kxa3 7.Kc5** and the pawn sails in to Queen.

61) 1...b6+! 2.axb6+ (2.Kb4 bxa5+ 3.Kxa5 Kb7 draws easily.) **2...Kb7 3.Kb4 Kxb6** drawing since Black holds the opposition.

62) 1.Kd5 Kc8 2.Ke6 Kb8 3.Kd7 Ka8 4.a6 Kb8! (Not 4...bxa6?? allowing 5.Kc7 and mate in three moves.) **5.a7+ Ka8** and stalemate is inevitable.

63) 1.Kd5 (After 1.b6+ Kd7 Black draws due to a stalemate defense–see example No.62.) **1...Kd7** (Also good are 1...Kc8 or 1...Kd8) **2.Ke5 Kc7** (Not 2...Ke7?? 3.a6, but 2...Kc8 or 2...Kd8 are also good.) **3.Ke6 Kd8 4.Kd6 Kc8 5.Ke7 Kc7 6.Ke8 Kc8** and White can't make any progress–draw.

64) 1...Kc4! (Restricting the White King.) **2.Kd2 Kd4 3.b3** (Or 3.a3 Kc4 4.Kc2 b5 5.b3+ Kc5 6.Kd3 Kd5 which is similar to our main line.) **3...Kc5 4.Kc3 Kb5 5.a3 Kc5 6.a4 b6 7.b4+ Kc6 8.Kc2** (Trying to obtain the "distant" opposition–see example No.27.) **8...Kc7** (Not 8...Kd5 9.Kd3 Kc6 10.Ke4 gaining the opposition and winning.) **9.Kd3 Kd7!** (Maintaining an odd number of squares between Kings–the "distant" opposition.) **10.Ke3 Ke7 11.Kf4 Kd6** (not 11...Kf6?? 12.a5) **12.Ke4 Ke6 13.Kd4 Kd6** and White is stymied–draw.

65) 1...Kc5 2. Ke4 Kc6 3.Kd4 Kb6 (3...Kd6 4.a4! wins.) **4.Kc4 Kc6 5.a4** and now we have reached the position after White's second move from example No.57 in which Black loses since he can't maintain the opposition.

66) **1...Kc4 2.Ke3** (Or 2.Kc2 Kd4 3.b4 axb3+ 4.axb3 with a drawn ending, as Black will retain the opposition.) **2...a3! 3.b3+** (3.bxa3 is drawn since the Black King can reach a8 to blockade.) **3...Kc3 4.Ke2 Kb2 5.b4 Kxa2 6.b5 Kb2 7.b6 a2 8.b7 a1=Q 9.b8=Q+** and it's a draw.

67) **1.b6 Kc8** (Not 1...axb6? 2.axb6 with an easy win.) **2.Kc6** (Of course, 2.bxa7 Kb7 draws for Black.) **2...Kb8 3.Kb5** (Or if 3.b7 then 3...a6 draws since 4.Kb6 is stalemate.) **3...axb6 4.axb6** (4.Kxb6 leaves the well-known drawing position–see No.28.) **4...Kb7** and Black draws easily since he holds the opposition.

68) **1.d4 Ke6 2.Ke4 d6** (2...d5+ 3.Kf4 Kf6 4.d3 Ke6 5.Kg5.) **3.d5+** (Not 3.d3? d5+! and Black can draw.) **3...Kf6 4.Kd4 Kf5 5.d3 Kf6 6.Kc3 Ke7** (6...Ke5 7.Kc4 Kf6 8.Kb5 wins) **7.Kb4** ("Outflanking" the Black King.) **7...Kd7 8.Kb5 Kc7 9.Ka6 Kd7 10.Kb7 Ke7 11.Kc6** and White wins.

69) **1...Ke5 2.Kc5 Ke4 3.Kd6 Kd4** (Counterattacking.) **4.c5 Kc4 5.c3 Kb5** and White can't make progress.

70) **1.b4 Kb8** (Or 1...Ka7 2.Kc6 Ka6 [hoping for 3.Kxc7 Kb5] 3.b5+! and wins.) **2.Kc6 Kc8 3.b5 Kb8** (Black's King has been relegated to passivity.) **4.b6 Kc8 5.b4** and White wins easily.

71) **1.Kc5** (Of course not 1.Kc6? stalemate.) **1...Kb7 2.a8=Q+! Kxa8 3.Kc6 Kb8 4.b7 Ka7 5.Kc7** and wins.

72) **1.Kb4 Kg8 2.Kc5 Kf7 3.Kd6 Ke8** (On 3...Kf6 4.Kxd7 Kxf5 5.Kxc6 and both sides Queen with a draw.) **4.c5! Kd8 5.f6!** A piquant resource; now after the forced **5...gxf6** it's stalemate.

73) **1.f4!** (Not 1.g3 Kc7 2.h4 Kd7 and the Black King can reach White's passer, while the White King is out of the "square" of Black's passer.) **1...Kc7** (Not 1...a5 2.f5 gxf5 3.h4! and White Queens.) **2.fxg5!!** (The point is to build a "stalemate fortress".) **2...a5 3.Kg3 a4 4.Kh4 a3 5.g3 a2** and it's stalemate.

74) **1.Kg4 Ke4 2.g6! h6** (Or 2...hxg6 3.fxg6 f5+ 4.Kg5 f4 5.h5 f3 6.h6 gxh6+ 7.Kxh6 and both sides Queen, with a draw.) **3.Kh5! Kxf5** stalemate.

75) **1.b6! axb6** (Or 1...cxb6 2.a6! bxa6 3.c6 and Queens.) **2.c6! bxc6 3.a6** and the pawn sneaks in to Queen.

76) 1.Kf7! h5! (A good try since 2.gxh5? is a theoretical draw as the Black King would block the h-pawns' advance.) **2.h4! Kh6** (2...hxg4 3.hxg5 Queens as does 2...gxh4 3.g5.) **3.Kf6 gxh4 4.g5+ Kh7 5.Kf7 h3 6.g6+ Kh6 7.g7** and wins.

77) 1.Kf6! (Not 1.Kh6? Ke6 2.Kg7 Kf5! 3.Kxf7 Kg4 4.Kxg6 Kxh4 and draws easily since the g-pawn falls, too.) **1...Ke8 2.Kg7 Ke7 3.g3 Ke6 4.Kf8 Kf6** (Or 4...f6 5.Kg7 Kf5 6.Kf7 g5 7.h5 wins.) **5.g4 Ke6 6.g5! f5 7.h5! f4 8.hxg6 f3 9.g7** and wins.

78) 1...b3! (Gaining space and preparing a favorable scenario for later .) **2.c3+ Ke4 3.Ke2 Kf4 4.Kf2 Kg4 5.Kf1 Kg3 6.Kg1 g4 7.Kf1 Kh2 8.Kf2 Kh1 9.Kg3 Kg1 10.Kxg4 Kxg2 11.Kf4 Kf2 12.Ke4 Ke2 13.Kd4 Kd2 14.Kxc4 Kc2** (Now the far advanced Black b-pawn will win, a result of 1...b3!.) **15.Kd4** (15.Kb4 Kxb2 16.Kxa4 Kc2 wins.) **15...Kxb2 16.c4 Kxa3 17.c5 b2 18.c6 b1=Q** wins.

79) 1.e7 Kf7 2.Kf3! (Not 2.Ke4 since 2...c5 3.Kd3 Ke8 4.Kc4 Kf7 is a drawn position.) **2...c6!** (Fighting for a tempo.) **3.Kf4! c5 4.Ke4!** (Winning the decisive tempo by "triangulation".) **4...Ke8 5.Kd3 Kf7 6.Kc4 Ke8 7.Kxc5 d3 8.Kd6 d2 9.Ke6** and White mates next.

80) 1.f4!! (In order to follow up with 2.d4.) **1...exf4 2.d4 Ke6** (Not 2...Kxd4?? 3.b6, but now the Black King has to take the "long way" around to White's b-pawn.) **3.Kg2 Kd7 4.Kf3 Kc7 5.Kxf4 Kb6 6.Ke4 Kxb5 7.Kd5** and **8.Kxd6** wins easily.

81) 1.Kc5 g5 (Or 1...Kg6 2.b4 Kf7 [trying to get in front of White's pawn] 3. b5 Ke7 4.Kc6! [4.Kb6? allows 4...g5 with a draw] 4...Kd8 5.Kb7 g5 6.b6 g4 7.Ka7 g3 8.b7 wins.) **2.b4 g4 3.Kd4 Kg5 4.b5 g3 5.Ke3 Kg4 6.b6 Kh3 7.b7 g2 8.Kf2 Kh2 9.b8=Q** with check, wins.

82) 1.f5! Kh6 2.Kxa6 Kg7 3.h5! (Otherwise 3...Kf6 would capture both pawns.) **3...Kf6 4.h6 Kf7 5.Kb6 Kf6 6.Kc6 Kf7 7.Kd7 Kf6 8.h7 Kg7 9.Ke7** and the f-pawn Queens.

83) 1.Ke7! (The obvious 1.Kf6 allows Black to draw after 1...e4! 2.c4+ Kd4 3.dxe4 Kxe4 4.c5 Kd5, etc.) **1...e4** (1...Kd4 2.Kd6 e4 3.dxe4 Kxe4 4.c4 and the c-pawn Queens) **2.c4+ Kd4 3.dxe4 Kxe4 4.Kd6 Kd4 5.c5** and Queens.

84) 1.Kf5 (Not 1.Kxg7?? h5 and Black wins.) **1...h5 2.Ke6 h4 3.Kd7 Kb7** (To stop Kc7.) **4.a8=Q+! Kxa8 5.Kc7** winning.

85) 1.c4! bxc3 2.bxc3 a3 3.c4 Kd7 4.e4 Kc7 5.e5! (Busting up Black's pawn chain.) **5...dxe5 6.Kxe5 Kc6 7.Ke6 Kc7 8.Kd5 Kb6 9.Kd6 Kb7 10.Kxc5 Kc7 11.Kb4 Kc6 12.Kxa3** wins.

86) 1.Kf5! (Not 1.h6? gxh6 2.Kf5 h5! 3.Kg5 Ke4 4.Kxh5 Kf5 with a draw, since White's King is trapped on the h-file, blocking his h-pawn.) **1...Kg3 2.h6! gxh6 3.h5 Kh4 4.Kg6 Kg4 5.Kxh6 Kf5 6.Kg7** winning.

87) 1.f4! Kb4 2.h4! (The pawns must cooperate.) **2...d5 3.f5 Kc5 4.h5 d4 5.f6 Kd6 6.h6! d3 7.f7 Ke7 8.h7 d2 9.f8=Q+ Kxf8 10.h8=Q+** winning.

88) 1.g6! (Not 1.h6+? Kh7 and Black can hold.) **1...Kh6 2.Kg4 Kg7** (Not 2...d3? 3.Kf3 and White will win the d-pawn.) **3.Kg5! d3 4.h6+ Kg8 5.Kf6! d2 6.h7+ Kh8 7.Kf7 d1=Q 8.g7+ Kxh7 9.g8=Q+ Kh6 10.Qg6#.**

KNIGHT AND PAWN ENDINGS

The Knight, a formidable warrior in the opening and middlegame, often comes into difficulties in Knight and pawn endings. This is because the Knight must make as many as four moves to cross the board–hence passed pawns can often simply outrun the Royal Steed. Nonetheless in certain types of these endings the Knight can pirouette with breathtaking verve, using checks (or the threat of check) to stop seemingly unstoppable pawns.

Though the Knight excels the Bishop in that it can control squares of both colors, it has the drawback of not being able to gain (or lose) a tempo, which is a trait the long-legged Bishop accomplishes with ease.

B   =

No.89

HINT: Almost any passed pawn can be stopped by a Knight if it can control the square in front of the pawn. However, an a- or h-pawn is often a problem for the Knight to stop.

EASY

W   =

No.90

HINT: The Knight can draw against an a- or h-pawn if the pawn isn't too far advanced.

EASY

W   + -

No.91

HINT: With an a- or h-pawn on the 7th rank, the Knight can't hold the draw when the enemy King is close enough to drive the Knight away.

EASY

B   =

No.92

HINT: If the a- or h-pawn is on the 6th rank, then a Knight can stop it from Queening even if the enemy King can support it; the Knight can always find a way to sacrifice itself for the pawn.

EASY

W   =

No.93

HINT: It seems hopeless for Black since his King seems to be too far away to help his Knight. The Black King can in fact help out.

MODERATE

W   =

No.94

HINT: The Black King, though far away, can come to the rescue in the nick of time.

EASY

W   =

No.95

HINT: White draws by rushing his Knight back–but there's only one right way.

DIFFICULT

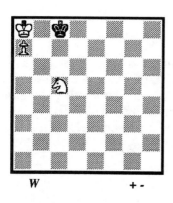

W   + -

No.96

HINT: White wins by forcing the Black King away.

EASY

B   =

No.97

HINT: Since a Knight cannot lose a move by maneuvering, with Black to move his King can "float" between c8 and c7, thereby shutting in the White King and drawing. Were it White's move, he would win with 1.Na6 or 1.Ne6 and the White King will be able to escape the corner and allow the pawn to promote.

EASY

W   =

No.98

HINT: An a- or h-pawn draws in positions of this type, since if the White King approaches to relieve the Knight of it's defensive duties, a stalemate occurs.

EASY

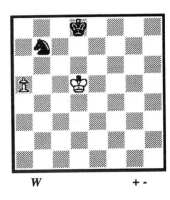

W   + -

No.99

HINT: This is another illustration of the difficulties a Knight has against an a- or h-pawn.

EASY

W   + -

No.100

HINT: White can force mate.

MODERATE

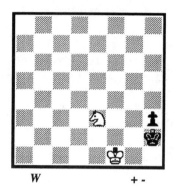

W   + -

No.101
HINT: White can force mate.

EASY

W   + -

No.102
HINT: White forces mate.

MODERATE

W   =

No.103
HINT: The White Knight proves nimble enough to catch the Black pawn.

EASY

B   =

No.104
HINT: Black draws with appropriate Knight moves. NOTE: Against a c- or f-pawn, the Knight can usually defend successfully.

MODERATE

W   =

No.105
HINT: The Knight can blockade the connected passers with accurate play. Then the White King can advance to win the pawns.

MODERATE

W   =

No.106
HINT: White's Knight maneuvers to blockade the pawns.

MODERATE

W　　　　　=

No.107
HINT: White draws by threats to sacrifice the Knight for the pawns, or forcing play into a drawn King and pawn ending.

EASY

B　　　　　=

No.108
HINT: Black draws by threats to sacrifice the Knight, winning both pawns or creating a drawn King and pawn ending.

MODERATE

W　　　　　=

No.109
HINT: White draws by accurate Knight maneuvers.

MODERATE

W =

No.110
HINT: White miraculously draws by perfectly timed Knight maneuvers to set up perpetual check.

DIFFICULT

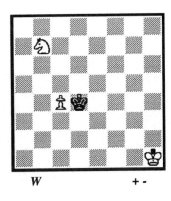

W + -

No.111
HINT: White wins by sacrificing the Knight to obtain a winning King and pawn ending.

DIFFICULT

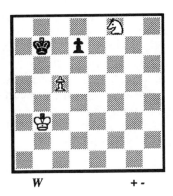

W + -

No.112
HINT: White again obtains a winning King and pawn ending by sacrificing his Knight.

DIFFICULT

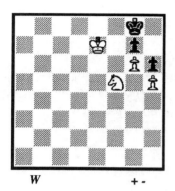

W　　　　　　+ -

No.113
HINT: White maneuvers to effect the correct Knight sacrifice; immediate sacrifices don't work.

DIFFICULT

W　　　　　　+ -

No.114
HINT: White forces mate.

MODERATE

B　　　　　　+ -

No.115
HINT: Black cannot draw. Generally speaking, an a- or h-pawn, as well as the b- or g-pawn give considerable difficulties to a Knight. With the c-, d-, e- or f-pawns, the Knight can usually defend successfully.

EASY

W   =

No.116
HINT: White draws by a subtle stalemate possibility.

DIFFICULT

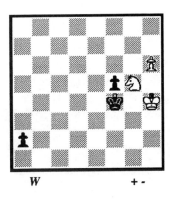

W   + -

No.117
HINT: Problem-like Knight maneuvers allow White's h-pawn to promote.

DIFFICULT

W   =

No.118
HINT: White diverts the Black Knight from the critical area and then deals with the h-pawn with his King and Knight.

DIFFICULT

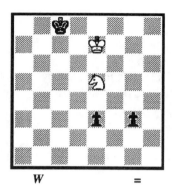

W   =

No.119
HINT: White draws with proper Knight maneuvers.

MODERATE

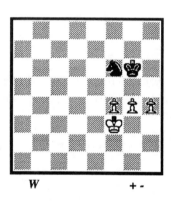

W   + -

No.120
HINT: White wins with three pawns vs the Knight if he can advance all three pawns to the 5th rank.

MODERATE

B   =

No.121
HINT: With the move Black can prevent White from advancing all three pawns to the 5th rank, thereby drawing.

DIFFICULT

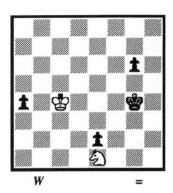

W =

No.122
HINT: Usually three widely separated pawns win vs the Knight, this is an exceptional case.

MODERATE

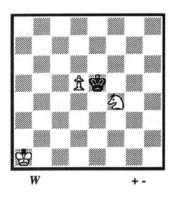

W + -

No.123
HINT: White wins since the Knight protects the pawn and the Black King can't capture as the pawn would Queen.

EASY

B =

No.124
HINT: With White to move, Black draws by shutting out the White King.

MODERATE

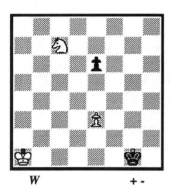

W   + -

No.125
HINT: White must combine protecting his pawn with a well-timed Knight sacrifice, eventually gaining the opposition and winning.

DIFFICULT

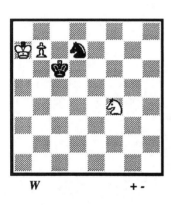

W   + -

No.126
HINT: Most Knight and pawn vs Knight endings are drawn. However, White wins here due to his well-placed King and far advanced pawn.

MODERATE

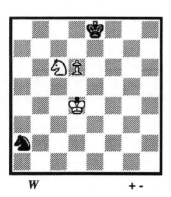

W   + -

No.127
HINT: White's well-placed Knight and far advanced pawn combined with Black's poorly placed Knight ensure the win.

DIFFICULT

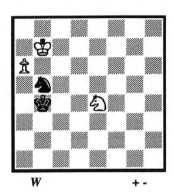

W   + -

No.128
HINT: As usual, a defending Knight has problems with an a- or h- pawn. Also, the well-placed White King accentuates Black's difficulties.

MODERATE

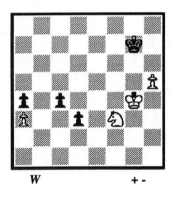

W   + -

No.129
HINT: Black can force the win of White's Knight, but then White's King can remain in control to obtain the win.

DIFFICULT

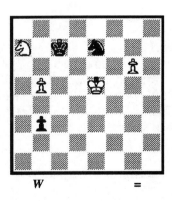

W   =

No.130
HINT: After a few moves it will seem like White is hopelessly lost, but a superb stalemate resource saves the day.

DIFFICULT

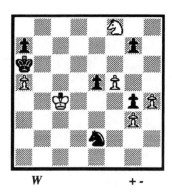

W   + -

No.131

HINT: The tactical motif of diversion is used at the beginning and the end, to force the Queening of White's pawn.

DIFFICULT

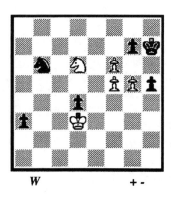

W   + -

No.132

HINT: Black's three passers are very dangerous, but White can win with a creative pattern of attack.

DIFFICULT

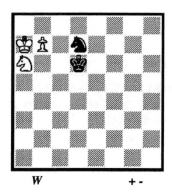

W   + -

No.133

HINT: A far advanced a-, b-, g- or h-pawn supported by their King and Knight usually win. Here White maneuvers to deflect Black's Knight.

DIFFICULT

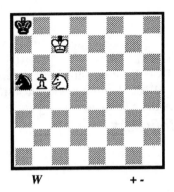

W + -

No.134
HINT: With the move, White forces the win with brisk tactical play (If Black is to move, it's a draw–see example No.135).

MODERATE

B =

No.135
HINT: With the move, Black can draw. This is because a Knight (The White Knight in this case.) can't change the tempo balance of the starting position by maneuvering (With White to move he would win–as in example No.134.).

DIFFICULT

W + -

No.136
HINT: As is so often the case, an a- or h- pawn gives the defender's Knight problems.

MODERATE

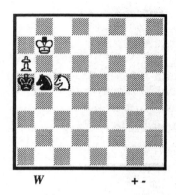

No.137
HINT: White's wins by diverting the Black Knight's vital control over the a7 square.

MODERATE

W   + -

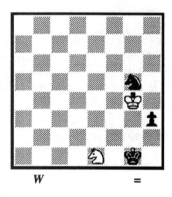

No.138
HINT: Black threatens 1...h2, Queening next; but neat tactics forestall Black's winning attempts.

MODERATE

W   =

SOLUTIONS FOR EXAMPLES 89-138

89) 1...Kf2 2.Nh3+ Kg3 3.Ng1 repeating the position and drawing. Also, on 1...Kh2 2.Nf3+ (or 2.Ne2) draws.

90) 1.Nc3+ Kb4 2.Nd5+ Kc4 3.Nb6+ Kb5 4.Nd5 and Black is getting nowhere since 4...a4 allows 5.Nc3+ followed by 6.Nxa4 drawing instantly. Also, 1.Nb2 Kb4 2.Nd3+ Kc3 3.Nc5 draws.

91) 1.Kc6 Na8 2.Kb7 Kc4 3.Kxa8 followed by 4.Kb7 wins.

92) 1...Na7 2.Kb6 Nc8+ 3.Kb7 Nd6+ 4.Kc7 Nb5+ (The Knight dances in circles, defying the White King.) **5.Kb6 Nd6!** the final trick; now 6.a7 allows 6...Nc8+ and 7...Nxa7.

93) 1.Kf6 (Going around, since the other obvious moves don't work: 1.Kd6 or 1.Kd4 allow 1...Nb5+ and 2...Nxa7.) **1...Kg3 2.Ke7 Kf4 3.Kd7 Na8 4.Kc8 Ke5 5.Kb7 Kd6 6.Kxa8 Kc7** stalemate. An important position to remember.

94) 1.Kf7 (1.Kd6 Nc8+ or 1.Ke7 Nc8+ and 2...Nxa7.) **1...Kg3 2.Ke8 Kf4 3.Kd8 Ke5 4.Kc7 Na8+ 5.Kb7 Kd6 6.Kxa8 Kc7** stalemate.

95) 1.Nf7! (The only move. The logical-looking 1.Ng6 loses: 1...h3 2.Nf4 h2 3.Ne2+ Kd2 4.Ng3 Ke1! 5.Kd6 Kf2 6.Nh1+ Kg2.) **1...h3 2.Ng5 h2 3.Ne4+ Kc2** (On 3...Kd4 4.Nf2! Kc3 [4...Ke3 5.Ng4+ and 6.Nxh2] 5.Kd6 Kd2 6.Ke5 Ke2 7.Nh1! Kf3 8.Kd4 Kg2 9.Ke3 Kxh1 10.Kf2 stalemate.) **4.Ng3 Kd1 5.Kd6 Ke1 6.Ke5 Kf2 7.Kf4** drawing.

96) 1.Na6 Kd8 (or d7) **2.Kb8** and Queens.

97) 1...Kc7 and draws since the Knight can't maneuver to change the tempo balance of a position: 2.Na6+ Kc8 3.Nb4 Kc7 4.Nd5+ Kc8 5.Nb6+ Kc7, etc., drawing.

98) 1.Kg6 stalemate. There is no way to make progress, even though White is a piece and pawn up!

99) 1.a6 Kc8 2.a7 and wins.

100) 1.Kf3! (1.Kf2? Kh1 leaves White in *zugzwang* since Black "threatens" ...h2 with stalemate and White's King and Knight can't cooperate quickly enough to win.) **1...Kh1 2.Kf2 Kh2** (2...h2 3.Ng3#) **3.Nc3 Kh1 4.Ne4 Kh2 5.Nd2 Kh1 6.Nf1 h2 7.Ng3#.**

101) 1.Kf2 Kh1 2.Nf1 h2 3.Ng3#.

102) 1.Ng3+ Kh2 2.Nf5 Kh1 3.Kf2! (A necessary temporizing move.) **3...Kh2 4.Ne3 Kh1 5.Nf1 h2 6.Ng3#.**

103) 1.Ne4+! Kc2 (1...Kc4 2.Nd2+ and 3.Nxb3 while 1...Kb4 2.Nd2 gets the Knight in front of the pawn–a theoretical draw.) **2.Nd6! b2 3.Nc4 b1=Q 4.Na3+** and **5.Nxb1** drawing.

104) 1...Nd7+ (Not 1...Ne6+, which loses to 2.Ke7 Nf4 3.Kf6 Nd5+ 4.Kf5 Ne7+ 5.Kg5 and the pawn Queens.) **2.Ke8** (2.Ke7 Ne5 3.f8=Q Ng6+ draws.) **2...Nf6+ 3.Kd8 Nh7** and draws since when the White King moves around to g6 (or h6) then Nf8 gives a theoretical draw.

105) 1.Nf3 b3 (Or 1...c3 2.Nd4 restraining the pawns, while if 1...Kh7 then 2.Ke7 or 2.Nd2 draws.) **2.Nd2 b2 3.Nb1 Kh7 4.Kf7 Kh6 5.Kf6 Kh5 6.Kf5 Kh4 7.Ke4 Kg4 8.Kd4** and White wins both pawns, drawing.

106) 1.Ng3 (Not 1.Nd2? c3 2.Nb3 d3 followed by ...d2, winning for Black.) **1...c3** (1...d3 2.Ne4.) **2.Ne2 c2 3.Nc1** and the White King moves down to pick off the pawns, drawing.

107) 1.Kb1 (Also drawing are 1.Nd5 or 1.Nc2+.) **1...c2+** (If 1...b2 2.Nd1 Kb3 3.Nxb2! cxb2 stalemate, or 1...Kb4 2.Nd5+ Kc4 3.Nxc3 Kxc3 4.Kc1 gains the opposition with an easy draw.) **2.Nxc2 bxc2+ 3.Kxc2** draw.

108) 1...Ng6! (Not 1...Nf5+? 2.Kd7 and 3.e7; or 1...Ke8 2.f7+! Kf8 3.e7+ Kxf7 4.Kd7 and 5.e8=Q; also losing is 1...Nf3 2.f7! [zugzwang] 2...Kg7 [2...Nd4 3.e7+ Kxf7 4.Kd7 and Queens] 3.Ke7 wins.) **2.Kd7** (2.f7 Ne7 draws, while 2.e7+ Nxe7! 3.fxe7+ Ke8 4.Ke6 stalemates.) **2...Ne5+ 3.Kd8 Nc6+ 4.Kc7 Nd4 5.Kd7** (5.e7+ Ke8 6.Kd6 Nf5+ 7.Ke6 Nxe7! 8.fxe7 stalemate.) **5...Nxe6! 6.Kxe6 Ke8** draws since Black holds the opposition.

109) 1.Ne6! g4 2.Ng7! f4 (2...g3 3.Nxf5 g2 4.Ne3+ draws.) **3.Nh5 f3 4.Nf6 g3** (Or 4...f2 5.Nxg4 f1=Q 6.Ne3+.) **5.Ne4 g2 6.Nd2+ Kd3 7.Nxf3** with a known drawing position–see example No. 89.

110) 1.Kf7! (Threat: 2.Nf6+ and 3.Nxe4.) **1...e3 2.Nf6+ Kh8 3.Nd5 e2 4.Nf4! e1=Q 5.Nxg6+ Kh7 6.Nf8+ Kh8 7.Ng6+** drawing by perpetual check.

111) 1.Na5! (The right way. The natural-looking 1.c5 allows 1...Kd5 2.Kg2 Kc6 3.Kf3 Kxb7 4.Ke4 Kc6 5.Kd4 Kc7 and Black retains the opposition, drawing.) **1...Kc5 2.Kg2 Kb4 3.Kf3 Kxa5 4.Ke4 Kb6 5.Kd5 Kc7 6.Kc5** and White obtains the opposition with a win.

112) 1.Kc4! (Not 1.Nxd7 Kc6 2.Kc4 Kxd7 3.Kd5 Kc7 holding the opposition, drawing.) **1...Kc6 2.Ng6 d6 3.Ne7+ Kd7 4.c6+! Kxe7 5.Kd5 Ke8 6.Ke6!** (Not 6.Kxd6? Kd8 and draws since 7.c7+ Kc8 8.Kc6 stalemates.) **6...Kd8 7.Kxd6 Kc8 8.c7 Kb7 9.Kd7** wins.

113) 1.Nd6 (1.Nxh6+ gxh6 2.Ke8 Kh8 draws due to stalemate, e.g., **3.Kf7**(or 3.Kf8) stalemates.) **1...Kh8 2.Ne4 Kg8 3.Ke8!** (In order to change the tempo balance.) **3...Kh8 4.Nf6! gxf6 5.Kf7** mating in three by 6.g7+, 7.g8=Q+, and 8.Qg6#.

114) 1.Nc6! bxc6 (Black's only move.) **2.Kc7 c5 3.b7+ Ka7 4.b8=Q+ Ka6 5.Qb6#.**

115) 1...Nd7+ (1...Nc6+ 2.Kc7 Nb4 3.Kb6 Nd5+ 4.Kb5 Nc7+ 5.Ka5 wins.) **2.Kc8** (Not 2.Kc7 since 2...Nc5! draws–3.b8=Q Na6+) **Nb6+ 3.Kd8** and Queens next.

116) 1.f7 Ke7 2.Ne6! Kxf7 3.Ng5+ Kf6 4.Nxf3 c2 5.Ng1! c1=Q stalemate.

117) 1.Ne6+ Ke3 (1...Ke4 2.Nc5+ and 3.Nb3 wins, or 1...Kf3 2.Nd4+ and 3.Nb3.) **2.Nd4!!** (The *idea* is to force Black's King to occupy the a1-h8 diagonal to facilitate the h-pawns advance.) **2...Kxd4** (2...a1=Q 3.Nc2+.) **3.h7 a1=Q 4.h8=Q+ and 5.Qxa1.**

118) 1.e6! (Diverting the Knight.) **1...Nc5+ 2.Ke2 Nxe6** (2...h2 3.e7 and both sides Queen with a draw.) **3.Kf1 h2 4.Ne2+ Kf3 5.Ng1+! Kg3** (Of course 5...hxg1=Q+ 6.Kxg1 is a draw.) **6.Ne2+ Kh3 7.Ng1+ Kg4 8.Kg2** wins the h-pawn, drawing.

119) 1.Nf3 g2 2.Ng1! (Not 2.Ke6 e2 3.Kf5 g1=Q 4.Nxg1 e1=Q.) **2...Kc7 3.Ke6 Kc6 4.Ke5 Kc5 5.Ke4** and White wins both pawns, drawing.

120) 1.f5+ (Not 1.g5 Nd5! 2.Ke4 Ne7 3.Ke5 Kh5! 4.f5 Kxh4 5.Kf6 [or 5.g6 Kg5 6.g7 Ng8–drawing] 5...Nd5+ 6.Kg6 Ne7+ and Black draws.) **1...Kg7 2.g5 Nd5 3.h5** (With all three pawns on the 5th, it's a theoretical win.) **3...Nc3 4.Kf4 Ne2+ 5.Ke5 Ng3 6.f6+ Kg8 7.h6 Nh5 8.g6 Ng3 9.h7+ Kh8 10.f7** and wins since 10...Kg7 is met by 11.f8=Q+ or 11.h8=Q+ as whichever Queen is captured allows the other pawn to Queen.

121) 1...Nd5 2.h5+ (Or 2.f5+ Kf6 3.Ke4 Nc3+ 4.Ke3 [4.Kd4 Nd1 threatening 5...Nf2 holds the draw] 4...Ke5 5.h5 Ne4 6.h6 Ng5 blockading the pawns, drawing.) **2...Kh6!** (Now on 3.g5+?? Kxh5.) **3.Ke4** (3.Kg3 Ne3 4.Kh4 Ng2+.) **3...Nf6+ 4.Kf5 Nd5** and White is stymied, since 5.Ke5 is met by 5...Ne3 winning a pawn, and there is no other way to make progress.

122) 1.Kd3 a3 2.Kxe2 a2 3.Nc2 Kg3 4.Kd2! Kf2 5.Kc3 g5 6.Kb2 g4 7.Nb4! g3 8.Nd3+ Kf3 (8...Ke2 9.Nf4+ Kf3 10.Nd3 draws as 10...g2 allows 11.Ne1+ and 12.Nxg2.) **9.Kxa2** draws since 9...g2 allows 10.Ne1+, or 9...Ke3 10.Ne1 Kf2 11.Nd3+ drawing–see example No.89.

123) 1.Kb2 Kd6 2.Kc3 Ke5 3.Kc4 Kd6 4.Kb5 Kd7 5.Kc5 Kc7 6.d6+ Kd8 7.Kc6 Kc8 8.Ne6 Kb8 9.d7 and Queens.

124) 1...Kg6 (Not 1...Kg4? 2.Kf6 Kf3 3.Kg5 Ke4 4.Ng7 winning.) **2.Ke5 Kg5 3.Ke4 Kg4** (3...Kg6 4.Kf4 Kf6 5.Nh4 Kg7 6.Kg5 winning.) and White can make no progress.

125) 1.e4! (After 1.Nxe6 Kf2 2.e4 Ke3 3.e5 Ke4 draws as does 3.Ng5 Kf4 or 3.Nc5 Kd4.) **1...Kf2** (1...e5 loses to 2.Nd5 Kf2 3.Kb2 Kf3 4.Nf6 protecting the e-pawn while bringing up the King, winning.) **2.Nd5!** (Guarding e3. Insufficient is 2.Nb5 Ke3 3.Nc3 Kd3! 4.Kb2 Kd2 5.Kb3 Kd3 6.Kb4 Kd4 and Black draws.) **2...Kf3** (Not 2...exd5? 3.exd5 Queening. Also, 2...Ke2 3.Nf6 Kd3 4.e5 Kd4 5.Nd7 wins after 5...Kd5 6.Kb2 Kc6 7.Nf6 Kc5 8.Kc3, etc.) **3.Nc3 Ke3 4.Ka2!** (To gain the opposition. After 4.Kb2 Kd2! or 4.Kb1 Kd3! Black gets the opposition, drawing–similar to the note after 2.Nd5!) **4...Kd4 5.Kb2!** (Not 5.Kb3? Kd3!.) **5...Kd3 6.Kb3 Kd4 7.Kb4 Kd3 8.Kc5! Kxc3 9.e5** (Now White has a winning King and pawn ending.) **9...Kd3 10.Kd6** and 11.Kxe6 winning.

126) 1.Ng6 (Threatening 2.Ne5+, removing the Nd7's control of b8.) **1...Kd5** (The only try. After 1...Kc5 2.Nf8 Ne5 3.Ka8 [3.b8=Q? Nc6+] Nc6 4.Ne6+ Kb6 5.Nd8! and White wins control of b8.) **2.Nf8 Ne5 3.Ka8 Nc6 4.Nd7 Kd6** (4...Ke6 5.Nb6 Kd6 6.Nc8+ Kc7 7.Na7 Nb8 8.Nb5+ wins.) **5.Nb6 Kc7 6.Nd5+ Kd8 7.Nb4 Kc7 8.Nxc6** winning.

127) 1.Kd5 Kd7 (1...Nc3+ 2.Ke6 wins as 3.d7 and 4.d8=Q can't be stopped.) **2.Nb8+!** (Not 2.Ne5+ Kc8 3.Nd3 Nc3+ 4.Kc6 Ne4 5.d7+ Kd8 6.Ne5 Ng5 with a draw.) **2...Kc8 3.Ke6 Nb4 4.d7+ Kc7** (4...Kd8 5.Kd6 and 6.Nc6#.) **5.Na6+ Nxa6 6.Ke7** Queening, with check, and winning.

128) 1.Kb6 Kc4 (1...Ka4 2.Nc3+! Nxc3 3.a7 Nd5+ 4.Kb7 wins.) **2.Nc3!** (Not 2.Nd6+? Nxd6 3.a7 Nc8+ and 4...Nxa7.) **2...Nd6 3.Kc7 Kc5 4.a7 Ne8+ 5.Kb8** wins.

129) 1.Kf4 d2 (On 1...c3 2.Ke3 d2 3.Ke2 Kh6 4.Kd1 Kxh5 5.Kc2 Kg4 6.Nd4 Kf4 7.Nb5 Ke3 8.Nxc3 wins easily.) **2.Nxd2 c3 3.Ke3!** (Now if 3...cxd2 then 4.Kxd2 Kh6 5.Kc3 Kxh5 6.Kb4 Kg6 7.Kxa4 Kf7 [trying to reach a8, with a theoretical draw] 8.Kb5 Ke7 9.Kb6 Kd7 10.Kb7 Kd6 11.a4 Kc5 12.a5 and Queens in three moves.) **3...c2 4.Nb3! axb3 5.Kd2 Kh6 6.a4 Kxh5 7.a5** and the a-pawn Queens.

130) 1.b6+ Kxb6 (On 1...Kb7 2.Nb5 followed by 3.Nc3 is a theoretical draw- see example No.89.) **2.Nc8+! Nxc8 3.Ke6! b2 4.g7 b1=Q 5.g8=Q Qb3+** (It seems lost for White.) **6.Kd7!!** and 6...Qxg8 creates stalemate. *Moral:* Never give up the ship!

131) 1.f6! (The first diversionary stroke.) **1...gxf6 2.h5 Nxg3 3.h6 Nf5 4.h7 Nd6+ 5.Kb4 Nf7 6.Ne6!** (With the artistic threat of 7.Nc5#.) **6...Kb7 7.Nd8+ Nxd8 8.h8=Q** wins.

132) 1.f7! Nd7 2.g6+ Kh8 (On 2...Kh6 3.f8=Q! Nxf8 4.Nf7#.) **3.Ne8 a2 4.f6** (Threat: 5.fxg7#.) **4...Ne5+ 5.Ke4** (Of course not 5.Kxd4 a1=Q+.) **5...Nxg6 6.fxg7+ Kh7 7.g8=Q+ Kh6 8.Qg7+ Kg5 9.f8=Q a1=Q 10.Qf4#.**

133) 1.Nb4 Ke5 (1...Kc7 2.Nd5+ Kd6 3.Nb6 Ne5 4.b8=Q+.) **2.Nd3+ Kd5** (2...Ke4 3.Nc5+ or 2...Kf5 3.Nc5 Ne5 4.Kb6 and queens.) **3.Nf4+ Kc6 4.Ng6 Kd5** (4...Kc5 5.Nf8 Ne5 6.Ka8 Nc6 7.Ne6+ Kd6 8.Nd8 deflects the Black Knight.) **5.Ka8 Kd6** (5...Nb6+ 6.Kb8 Kd6 7.Nf8 Kc6 8.Ka7 wins.) **6.Nf8 Nb6+ 7.Ka7** Queens.

134) 1.b6 Nb7! (Since 2.Nxb7 is stalemate.) **2.Ne6! Na5** (2...Nd8, hoping for 3.Nxd8 stalemate, is met by 3.Kc8! since 3...Nxe6 4.b7+ Queens and 3...Nc6 (or b7) allows 4.Nc7#. Note that 2...Nd8 should not be met by 3.Kxd8 as 3...Kb7! wins the pawn, drawing.) **3.Kc8! Knight anywhere 4.Nc7#.**

135) 1...Nc4 2.Nd3 Ka7 3.Nb4 Ka8 4.Nd5 Ka7 5.Ne7 Ka8 6.Nc6 (White hopes to now be able to push the b-pawn to win, but Black has a surprising defense.) **6...Nb6!!** and draws since 7.Kxb6 stalemates.

136) 1.Nd5! (Stopping 1...Ne7.e.g., if 1.Nb5 then 1...Ne7 stopping 2.a7 because of 2...Nc8+ and 3...Nxa7.) **1...Kd6 2.Ne3! Kd7** (2...Ne7 3.Nf5+! Nxf5 4.a7 Queens.) **3.Nc4** (Threat: 4.Ne5+ Nxe5 5.a7.) **3...Ne7 4.Kb7 Nc8 5.Nb6+ Nxb6 6.Kxb6 Kc8 7.a7** Queens.

137) 1.Ne4! Kb4 (1...Ka4 2.Nc3+! Nxc3 3.a7.) **2.Kb6 Ka4** (If 2...Kc4 then not 3.Nd6+ Nxd6 4.a7 Nc8+, but instead 3.Nc3! Kxc3 [3...Nxc3 4.a7 Nd5+ 5.Kb7] 4.Kxb5 and 5.a7 winning.) **3.Nc3+! Nxc3 4.a7 Nd5+ 5.Kb7** and **6.a8=Q.**

138) 1.Nf3+! (Since 1...Nxf3 2.Kxh3 draws.) **1...Kg2** (Hoping for 2.Nxg5 h2.) **2.Nh4+ Kf2 3.Nf3!** drawing as 3...Nxf3 allows 4.Kxh3.

BISHOP AND PAWN ENDINGS

Aside from Rook and pawn endings, the theory of Bishop and pawn endings is among the most intricate of all types of endings. The Bishop's two main strengths (especially compared to the Knight) is that it is a long range piece and it can gain or lose a tempo by appropriate maneuvering. Its long range is very effective in restraining or catching enemy passed pawns, while its main drawback is that it can control squares of only one color. This can allow the defender to set up a complete blockade against the Bishop's actions on squares of the opposite color.

With Bishops of opposite colors a player who is two (or occasionally even three) pawns down can effect an airtight blockade forcing the materially superior side to concede the draw. Opposite colored Bishops, however, do not by any means guarantee the draw–there are a number of positions which can be won with proper technique.

W =

No.139

HINT: This is a frequently occurring theoretical draw. White's Bishop is the "wrong color", i.e., it can't control the critical a8 square in order to Queen the a-pawn. Black's King simply stays in or directly adjacent to the a8 square; if White approaches too close with his King, trying to drive out the Black King, then it's stalemate.

EASY

W =

No.140

HINT: Black draws by blockading the b7 square; the possibility of stalemate allows successful defense.

EASY

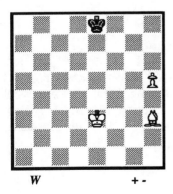

W + -

No.141

HINT: Here we have an exception to the "wrong color" Bishop vs the h- (or a-) pawn drawing position—see example No. 139.

MODERATE

W   + -

No.142

HINT: A clever tactic prevents capture of the pawn and leads to its promotion.

MODERATE

W   + -

No.143

HINT: White wins by intercepting the diagonal of the Bishop, which allows the pawn to Queen.

EASY

B   =

No.144

HINT: Black to move can draw by preventing White from successfully intercepting the Black Bishop's diagonal control of the d7 square.

EASY

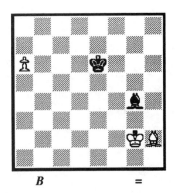

B   **=**

No.145
HINT: Black can draw by precise tactics.

MODERATE

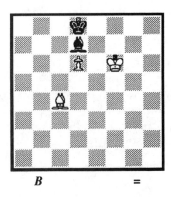

B   **=**

No.146
HINT: Black's drawing method is simple: his King sits at d8 while the Black Bishop shuttles about, marking time. The blockade is unbreakable as the White Bishop can't control d8.

EASY

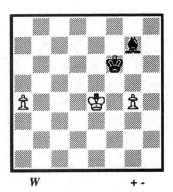

W   **+ -**

No.147
HINT: If two pawns (At least one file apart.) are not yet beyond the 4th rank, the Bishop can usually stop them. Here is an exceptional case.

DIFFICULT

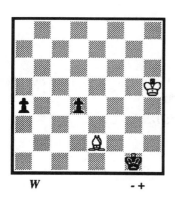

W   - +

No.148

HINT: If two pawns (At least two files apart.) are on the 5th rank, they usually win.

MODERATE

W   =

No.149

HINT: Sometimes two passed pawns (At least one file apart.) on the 5th rank can be stopped. The key here is the excellent position of the defending Bishop.

EASY

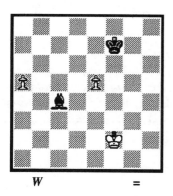

W   =

No.150

HINT: In some cases, two pawns which are three files apart on the 5th rank can be stopped by a properly placed Bishop.

EASY

B   - +

W   =

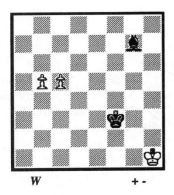

W   + -

No.151
HINT: With two pawns two files apart and one of them on the 5th rank (The other pawn on the 4th.) , the defending King must be properly positioned in front of the pawns to hold the draw. Here White's King isn't in front of the pawns, so he loses.

MODERATE

No.152
HINT: Two connected passed pawns can usually be stopped by a Bishop (Assuming the enemy King is not too near.), if they are no farther advanced than the 5th rank.

EASY

No.153
HINT: The unfavorable position of the Bishop allows White to win.

EASY

B   =

No.154
HINT: Black draws by keeping the Bishop on the right diagonal.

EASY

B   =

No.155
HINT: If not all of three connected passed pawns have reached the 5th rank, then the defending Bishop can usually draw.

MODERATE

B   - +

No.156
HINT: This is identical to example No.155, except the White Bishop is poorly placed in front of the pawns. This allows Black to win.

DIFFICULT

B   - +

No.157
HINT: Preliminary King maneuvers followed by a diversionary pawn sacrifice give Black the win.

MODERATE

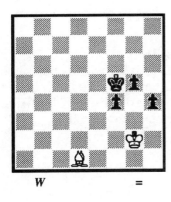

W   =

No.158
HINT: White can draw by blockading the Black pawns.

EASY

B   =

No.159
HINT: White's King gets back just in time to help his Bishop hold against the pawns.

MODERATE

W   + -

No.160
HINT: Important rule: the defender's Bishop can stop the enemy pawn if it has at least three squares on the diagonal which controls a square in front of the pawn. In this example, there are only two squares available on the a6-c8 diagonal, so Black loses.

EASY

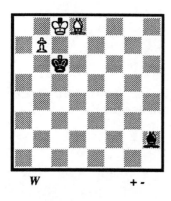

W   + -

No.161
HINT: White wins by finessefully maneuvering his Bishop to eventually block the Black Bishop's control of b8.

DIFFICULT

B   =

No.162
HINT: A beautiful stalemate resource holds the draw for Black.

MODERATE

W   + -

No.163

HINT: White can't win if the Black King is allowed to reach a8, so he must keep Black's King at bay while maneuvering to win Black's a-pawn.

DIFFICULT

W   + -

No.164

HINT: White must avoid several drawing tricks in order to win.

DIFFICULT

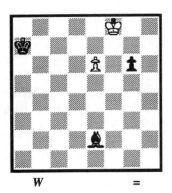

W   =

No.165

HINT: It seems Black's g-pawn must Queen, while White's e-pawn can be easily stopped by the Bishop, but White can draw nonetheless!

DIFFICULT

No.166
HINT: White combines threats to enter the "square" of the b-pawn with threats to Queen his c-pawn, in order to draw.

DIFFICULT

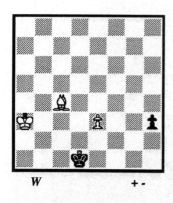

No.167
HINT: A tactical trick at the end enables White to win.

DIFFICULT

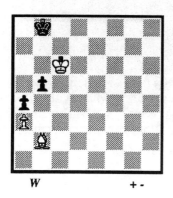

No.168
HINT: White wins by using *zugzwang* to force Black's b-pawn to advance, thus allowing White to convert his a-pawn into a "better" b-pawn.

DIFFICULT

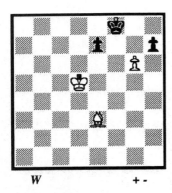

W + -

No.169
HINT: White constructs a mating attack with minimal material.

DIFFICULT

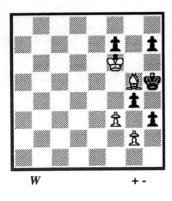

W + -

No.170
HINT: White can force mate.

DIFFICULT

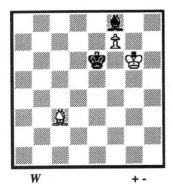

W + -

No.171
HINT: White wins by man-euvering his King to g8, then the White Bishop can deal the final blow.

MODERATE

B   =

No.172
HINT: Black's King is in a favorable position, enabling him to draw.

MODERATE

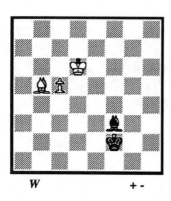

W   + -

No.173
HINT: White wins by intercepting the diagonal of Black's Bishop to clear the way for the c-pawn.

MODERATE

W   =

No.174
HINT: Black's King is very well-placed (Attacking the f-pawn and holding the opposition.), he can therefore draw.

EASY

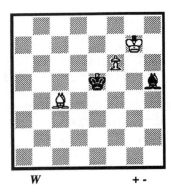

W   + -

No.175

HINT: This example should be compared to No.174. There Black drew because his King was next to the enemy pawn and he held the "direct" opposition (This means opposition along a file or a rank.) Here the Black King has the "diagonal" opposition (This is just like the regular opposition, except it's along a diagonal.) Unfortunately for Black diagonal opposition in this type of position loses.

EASY

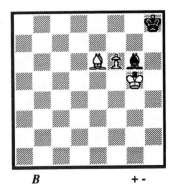

B   + -

No.176

HINT: The poor position of Black's King gives White the win.

MODERATE

B   =

No.177

HINT: Black must shift his King to the right square to prevent White from maneuvering his Bishop to f6.

MODERATE

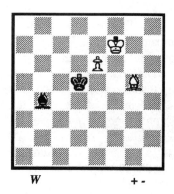

W　　　　　　　+ -

No.178

HINT: Black draws if he can get his King to f5 in time to stop a timely White Bf6. Here Black can't get there in time–and loses.

MODERATE

B　　　　　　　=

No.179

HINT: Black draws because White can't challenge the a1-h8 diagonal, to enable his pawn to Queen.

EASY

W　　　　　　　+ -

No.180

HINT: White maneuvers his Bishop to eventually neutralize the Black Bishop's defensive functions.

MODERATE

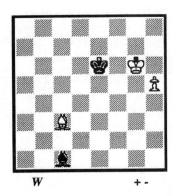

W + -

No.181

HINT: This is a draw, since after White plays Bh6, Black can trade Bishops and rush his King in front of the h-pawn or block in the White King.

MODERATE

B =

No.182

HINT: Black draws by attacking the g-pawn.

EASY

W + -

No.183

HINT: White wins by removing the Black Bishop's control of g8.

EASY

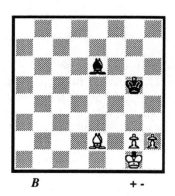

B   + -

No.184
HINT: White wins with connected passers, but there is a drawing trick White must avoid.

MODERATE

B   =

No.185
HINT: Black draws by exploiting stalemate possibilities.

DIFFICULT

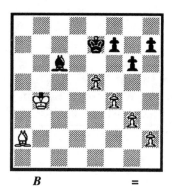

B   =

No.186
HINT: Black can draw a pawn down since his King sits on a fine blockading square.

MODERATE

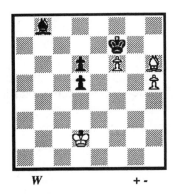

W   + -

No.187
HINT: White uses problem-like Bishop maneuvers to force the win.

DIFFICULT

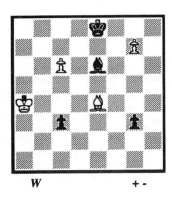

W   + -

No.188
HINT: White wins with precise tactical play.

DIFFICULT

B   - +

No.189
HINT: Black's "good" Bishop can attack White's pawns, but White's "bad" Bishop can't emulate. This plus clever tactics force the win.

MODERATE

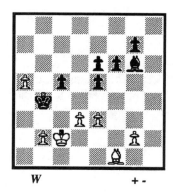

W   + -

No.190
HINT: White's advanced a-pawn and some brilliant tactics create a win.

DIFFICULT

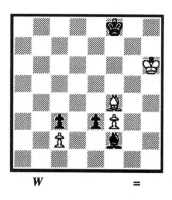

W   =

No.191
HINT: Both sides exhibit clever tactics–the result, a pleasing draw by stalemate.

MODERATE

W   + -

No.192
HINT: White sacrifices his Bishop to Queen a pawn.

DIFFICULT

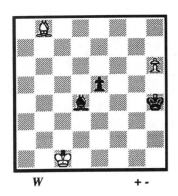

W   + -

No.193
HINT: White produces crisp tactics, culminating in the blockade of e4, which allows the h-pawn to Queen.

DIFFICULT

B   =

No.194
HINT: Black draws by stalemate.

EASY

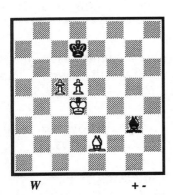

W   + -

No.195
HINT: Opposite colored Bishops often allow the weaker side to draw, but here the relatively poor position of Black's Bishop gives White a win.

MODERATE

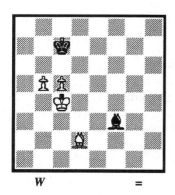

W   =

No.196
HINT: This is just like example No. 195, but shifted one file to the left. This leaves White unable to "outflank" Black on the Queenside as in No.195.

MODERATE

SOLUTIONS FOR EXAMPLES 139-196

139) 1.a6 Kb8 2.Be5+ Ka8 (Of course not 2...Kc8?? 3.a7.) **3.Kc6 Ka7 4.Kb5 Ka8 5.Bd4** (Note: 5.Kb6 stalemates.) **5...Kb8** and White is getting nowhere–draw.

140) 1.Kd6 Ka8 and now trying to control b7 by 2.Kc6 or 2.Kc7 is stalemate, therefore no progress is possible–draw.

141) 1.Be6! ("Fencing-off" the Black King from reaching the h8 square, which would allow Black to draw.) **1...Ke7 2.h6 Kf6 3.Bf5! Kf7 4.Bh7!** (Preventing Kg8-h8.) **4...Kf6** (Threatening 5...Kg5 and 6...Kxh6.) **5.Kf4 Kf7 6.Kg5 Kf8 7.Kf6 Ke8 8.Kg7** controlling h7 and h8, thus assuring the Queening of the h-pawn.

142) 1.Bd5! (The only way to stop Black from drawing with Kc4, capturing the pawn.) **1...Kxd5 2.Kb5** with a won King and pawn ending,e.g., **2...Kd6 3.c4 Kd7** (3...Kc7 4.Kc5 with the opposition.) **4.Kb6**, etc., winning.

143) 1.Bf3 Ba4 (Or 1...Ke8 2.Bc6+ Bxc6 3.Kxc6 Kd8 4.d7 Ke7 5.Kc7 wins.) **2.Bc6 Bxc6 3.Kxc6 Ke8 4.Kc7** and Queens in two moves.

144) 1...Kc5! (Controlling c6 while tying the White King to the defense of the pawn.) **2.Bg4 Ba4 3.Bd7 Bd1 4.Bc6 Bg4** this last move completes the drawing method–Black's Bishop switches to another diagonal to maintain control of the d7 square.

145) 1...Bf5 2.Kf3 (2.a7 Be4 draws.) **2...Bd3! 3.a7 Bc4 4.a8=Q Bd5+** drawing.

146) 1...Bc6 (Or almost any other square.) **2.Be6 Bb5** (Or almost any other square.) and White has no way to make progress.

147) 1.a5 Bf8 2.Kd5 (Stopping 2...Bc5 and threatening 3.a6.) **2...Bh6 3.g5+!! Bxg5** (On 3...Kxg5 4.a6 promotes the pawn since the Kg5 blocks the Bh6 from reaching e3.) **4.Ke4 Bh4 5.Kf3!** and a6-a7-a8=Q can't be stopped.

148) 1.Bc4 a3 (Threatening 2...d3 3.Bxd3 a2.) **2.Kg4 Kf2 3.Kf4 d3 4.Ke4 d2 5.Bb3 a2** and a pawn Queens.

149) The Bishop on b5 holds up the two pawns. There is no way for White to successfully advance them. A Black Bishop on b7 would do equally well here. **1.Kf4 Ke6 2.Ke4 Kd7 3.Kd5 Kc7** and White cannot make further progress–draw.

150) 1.Ke3 Ke6 2.Kd4 Ba6 draws easily, since 3.Kc5 Kxe5 is obviously drawn and other moves make no progress. NOTE: The Bishop could also draw from c8 in our original position.

151) 1...f4 2.Kb4 f3 3.Be1 Kd4 4.Ka3 (Trying to get in front of the pawns.) **4...c3 5.Ka2** (5.Kb3 Kd3 6.Bxc3 f2.) **5...Kd3 6.Kb1 Ke2 7.Bh4** (7.Bxc3 f2.) **7...Kd1** and the Bishop can no longer hold the pawns.

152) 1.b6 (On 1.c6 Bd8 effectively holds up the pawns.) **1...Bd4 2.b7 Be5** and the pawns are restrained. In this case they soon fall as the Black King will get to them quickly.

153) 1.c6 Be5 (If the Bishop were on, say, f6 [or any other square on the d8-h4 diagonal] then 1.c6 could be met by 1...Bd8, drawing.) **2.b6** wins as 3.c7 and 4.c8=Q is unstoppable.

154) 1...Ba8 (But not 1...Bc8?? 2.b6 and 3.b7 winning.) **2.c7 Bb7** with a secure blockade, drawing.

155) 1...f3+ 2.Kf2 Kf4 3.Bxg5+! (Transposing into a drawn King and pawn ending.) **3...Kxg5 4.Kxf3** and Black can't stop the White King from reaching h1–an elementary drawing position. If 4...h3 5.Kg3 wins the h-pawn.

156) 1...Kf5 (On 1...f3+ 2.Kg1!! draws: 2...Kf5 3.Ba5 g4 4.Bd8 h3 5.Bc7 Ke4 6.Kf2 and White holds an airtight blockade, drawing.) **2.Ba5** (On 2.Kh3 Ke4! 3.Kg4 Ke3 4.Kxg5 h3 and the h-pawn Queens.) **2...g4 3.Bd8 h3+ 4.Kh2 Ke4 5.Bb6 Kf3 6.Bc7 Ke3 7.Bb8 f3 8.Kg1 Ke2 9.Bg3 h2+! 10.Kxh2 f2 11.Bxf2 Kxf2 12.Kh1 Kg3 13.Kg1 Kh3 14.Kh1 g3 15.Kg1 g2 16.Kf2 Kh2** and Queens.

157) 1...Kc2 2.Ba5 Kd1 3.Kf2 g1=Q+! 4.Kxg1 e1=Q+ 5.Bxe1 Kxe1 and the f-pawn Queens.

158) 1.Kh3 Ke4 2.Kg2 Ke3 3.Bg4 f3+ 4.Bxf3 h3+ 5.Kg3 with an iron-clad blockade–draw.

159) 1...Kf5 (1...e4 2.Kc4 Kf5 3.Kd4 b5 4.Bd6 b4 5.Bxb4 Kf4 6.Be1 Kf3 7.Bh4 e3 8.Kd3 g3 9.Bxg3 Kxg3 10.Kxe3.) **2.Kc4!** (Not 2.Kb6 e4 3.Kc5 b5 4.Kd4 b4 5.Bh2 b3 6.Kc3 e3 7.Kxb3 e2 8.Bg3 Ke4 9.Kc3 Kf3 10.Be1 g3 11.Bxg3 Kxg3 12.Kd2 Kf2 wins for Black.) **2...Ke4 3.Kc5 b5 4.Bh2!** (4.Kxb5? Kd4! wins.) **4...b4 5.Kc4 b3 6.Kxb3 Kd4 7.Kc2 e4 8.Kd2** and the White King has returned in time to help the Bishop, drawing.

160) 1.Bh3 (Any other move–except 1.Bc8??–also wins.) **1...Kb5 2.Bf1+** wins.

161) 1.Bh4 Kb5 2.Bf2 (Trying to play Ba7-b8.) **2...Ka6! 3.Bc5!** (Stopping 3...Bd6. On 3.Be3 Black would have 3...Bd6! 4.Bg5 Kb5 5.Bd8 Kc6 stopping 6.Bc7.) **3...Bf4 4.Be7 Kb5 5.Bd8 Kc6 6.Bg5!** (White's maneuvers have gained a decisive tempo.) **6...Bh2 7.Be3 Kb5 8.Ba7 Ka6 9.Bb8 Bg1 10.Bg3** (Or d6/e5/f4.) **10...Ba7 11.Bf2!** wins as White gains control of b8 by force.

162) 1...Bd8! drawing since 2.e8=Q or 2.e8=R is stalemate.

163) 1.Kb7! Kb5 2.Bb6 Kc4 3.Kc6 Kb3 4.Bc5 Kc4 5.Be3 Kb3 6.Bc1! Kc4 (6...Kc2 7.Kb5! Kxc1 8.Kxa4 Kb2 9.Kb4 and the a-pawn sails in .) **7.Bb2! Kb3 8.Kb5! Kxb2 9.Kxa4 Kc3 10.Kb5 Kd4 11.a4 Kd5 12.a5 Kd6 13.Kb6 Kd7 14.a6** and the a-pawn Queens in two moves.

164) 1.Kd4!! (Not 1.Kc5? b6+! since 2.Bxb6+ Kb7 and the King reaches a8, drawing. On 2.axb6 Kb7 is another theoretical draw–see example No.140. Or if 1.Kc4? then 1...b5+! draws since 2...Kb7 can't be stopped.) **1...Kc6** (1...b5 2.a6! Kc6 3.Kc3 Kd7 4.Kb4 Kc6 5.Ka5 Kd7 6.Kxb5 Kd6 7.Bb8+ Kd7 8.Kb6 Kc8 9.Bf4 wins easily.) **2.Bb6! Kd6** (2...Kb5 3.Kd5 Ka6 4.Kd6 Kb5 5.Kc7 Ka6 6.Kb8 Kb5 7.Kxb7 wins.) **3.Kc4 Kc6 4.Kb4 Kd6**

5.Kb5 Kd7 6.Kc5 Kc8 7.Ba7 (Stopping K-b8-a8.) **7...Kc7 8.Kb5 Kd7 9.Bb8 Kc8 10.Bh2 Kd7 11.Kb6 Kc8 12.Bg3 Kd7 13.Kxb7** winning.

165) 1.Ke7! (Threatening to catch the g-pawn with 2...Kf6.) **1...g5 2.Kd6! g4 3.e7 Bb5 4.Kc5 Bd7 5.Kd4** (Now White's King has finagled his way into the "square" of the g-pawn.) **5...Kb6 6.Ke4 Kc6 7.Kf4 Kd6 8.e8=Q Bxe8 9.Kxg4** draw.

166) 1.Kc8! b5 2.Kd7 (Planning 3.Kc6, which would threaten both 4.c8=Q and 4.Kxb5.) **2...Bf5+** (Or 2...b4 3.Ke6 Kf4 4.Kd5 Bf5 5.Kc4 drawing.) **3.Kd6 b4 4.Ke5 Kg4 5.Kd4 b3 6.Kc3 Be6 7.c8=Q Bxc8 8.Kxb3** draws.

167) 1.Bd5 Ke2 (1...h2 2.Bh1! [not 2.Bg2 Ke1 3.e4 Kf2 4.Bh1 Kg1 5.Bf3 Kf2 draws] 2...Ke2 3.e4 Kf2 4.e5 Kg1 5.Ba8 wins.) **2.e4 Ke3 3.e5 Kd4 4.e6 Kxd5 5.e7 h2 6.e8=Q h1=Q 7.Qa8+** winning Black's Queen.

168) 1.Be5+ (Not 1.Kxb5?? [which allows Black an elementary draw by simply keeping his King on, or directly next to a8] as after White captures the a4 pawn, he would remain with the "wrong–color" Bishop to Queen the a3 pawn.) **1...Ka7** (1...Kc8 2.Bc7 b4 3.axb4 a3 4.b5 a2 5.b6 a1=Q 6.b7#.) **2.Bc7 Ka8** (2... Ka6 3.Bb6 b4 4.axb4 a3 5.b5#.) **3.Kb6! b4 4.axb4 a3 5.b5 a2 6.Be5 a1=Q 7.Bxa1** winning easily.

169) 1.Bh6+ Kg8 2.g7 Kf7 (2...e6+ 3.Kd6! Kf7 4.Ke5 Kg8 5.Kf6! e5 6.Ke6 [6.Kxe5 Kf7 draws] 6...e4 7.Kf6 e3 8.Bxe3 h5 9.Bg5 h4 10.Bxh4 Kh7 11.Kf7 Queens.) **3.g8=Q+!** (Not 3.Ke5? e6 4.Kd6 e5! 5.Kxe5 Kg8–a theoretical draw due to a stalemate defensive method.) **3...Kxg8 4.Ke6 Kh8 5.Kf7! e5 6.Bg7#.**

170) 1.g3! (1.Kf5? g3!) **1...h6** (1...gxf3 2.Kf5 and 3.g4#.) **2.Be3 h2 3.Kf5 gxf3 4.Bf2! h1=Q 5.g4#.**

171) 1.Bg7 Bb4 (1...Ke7 2.Bf6+ Ke6 3.Bg5 Bb4 4.Kg7 transposes into our main line.) **2.Bh6 Bc5 3.Kg7 Bb4** (3...Kf5 4.Kg8 Kg6 5.Bf8 Be3 6.Bb4 Bh6 7.Bc3! Kf5 8.Bg7 wins.) **4.Kg8 Bc5 5.Bf8 Be3 6.Bb4 Bh6 7.Bd2!** wins.

172) 1...Be5 2.Ba3 Bg7 3.Bb2 Bh6 4.Bc1 Bg7 5.Bd2 Kd6 (Or 5...Kf5.) and White can make no progress, so it's a draw. NOTE: King position is very important: if the White King could get to g8, White would win.

173) 1.Bc6 Be2 2.Bd5 Bb5 (Forced.) **3.Be6 Ke3 4.Bd7 Ba6** (4...Bf1 5.c6 Kd4 6.c7 Ba6 7.Kc6 Kc3 8.Kb6 driving off the Bishop and winning.) **5.c6 Kd4 6.c7 Kc4 7.Bh3 Kb4 8.Kc6 Ka5 9.Bg4 Kb4 10.Kb6** wins. NOTE: The Black King was too far away to help.

174) 1.Bf7 Be2 2.Bg6 Bc4 3.Bh7 Bb3 4.Bg8 Bxg8 5.Kxg8 Kxf6 draw.

175) 1.Bd3 Kf4 (There's nothing better. The Black King rushes to g5 to obtain "direct" opposition, but there isn't enough time.) **2.Bg6** and the f-pawn will Queen.

176) 1...Bd3 (1...Kh7 2.Bf5 Bxf5 3.Kxf5 Kg8 4.Kg6 Kf8 5.f7 Ke7 6.Kg7. Also, 1...Be8 2.Kf5 Kh7 3.Bd5 Bh5 [3...Bd7+ 4.Ke5 Kg6 5.f7 Kg7 6.Kd6 Bf5 7.Ke7 Queens] 4.Ke6 Kg6 5.Ke7 Kf5 6.Bf7 Bd1 7.Be6+ and 8.f7 wins.) **2.Kf4 Bb5 3.Ke5 Be8 4.Kd6 Kh7 5.Ke7 Kg6 6.Bd7 Bf7 7.Bf5+! Kxf5 8.Kxf7 Ke5 9.Ke7** Queens shortly.

177) 1...Ke4! (On the way to f5. Wrong is 1...Ke5? 2.Be7 Bd2 3.Bf6+ and 4.e7, winning.) **2.Be7 Be1 3.Ba3 Bh4 4.Bb2 Kf5!** (Stopping 5.Bf6.) and it's a draw.

178) 1.Be7 Bd2 2.Ba3 Bg5 3.Bb2! Ke4 (Too late!) **4.Bf6 Bxf6 5.Kxf6** and the pawn Queens.

179) 1...Bc3 (Or a1/b2/e5/g7.) and by simply moving his Bishop along the a1-h8 diagonal, Black draws easily as White can't interpose his Bishop on that diagonal.

180) 1.Bg7 (Heading for h6.) **1...Bd2 2.Bh6 Bb4** (2...Bxh6 3.Kxh6 Kf5 4.Kg7 Queens in 3 moves.) **3.Be3 Bf8** (Or 3...Bc3 4.h6 Ba1 5.h7 Bc3 6.Bh6 Ba1 7.Bg7 winning.) **4.Bd4 Kh4 5.Be5!** (Temporizing.) **5...Kg4 6.Bf6 Kf4 7.Bg7 Ba3 8.h6** Queens in 2 moves.

181) 1.Bg7 Bd2 2.Bh6 Bxh6! 3.Kxh6 Kf7 (With the idea of K-g8-h8, an elementary draw.) **4.Kh7 Kf8** (Blocking in the White King. If White tries to escape with Kg6, then K-g8-h8.) **5.h6 Kf7 6.Kh8 Kf8 7.h7** stalemate.

182) 1...Kg3 2.Bf3 Bc4 and White can't stop 3...Bf1 and 4...Bxf2 drawing.

183) 1.Bf7 Bh7 2.Kg5 Ke7 3.Kh6 Kxf7 4.Kxh7 and Queens.

184) 1...Bh3! (A good try. Now 2.gxh3?? is a draw since only h-pawns are left allowing Black to draw by sending his King to h8.) **2.g3** (Black threatened 2...Bxg2!) **2...Kh6 3.Bf1 Bg4 4.h4 Bf5 5.Kf2 Bg4 6.Ke3 Be6 7.Kf4 Bd7 8.Bd3 Bh3 9.Bf5** (Not 9.g4? Bxg4!) **9...Bf1 10.g4** (Finally!) **10...Be2 11.g5+ Kh5 12.Kg3** (Not 12.g6? Kh6 13.Ke5 Bh5 14.Kf6 Bxg6! 15.Bxg6 stalemate.) **12...Bd1 13.Be4 Bb3 14.Bf3+ Kg6 15.Kf4 Bf7 16.h5+ Kg7 17.Ke5 Bb3 18.Be4 Bf7 19.h6+ Kh8 20.Kf6 Bh5 21.Bd5 Kh7 22.Bf7 Bf3 23.g6+ Kxh6 24.g7** wins. Obviously there were other moves at "non-critical" moments which would lead to a win; the main idea throughout was to avoid a drawing sacrifice of Black's Bishop.

185) 1...Bd5! (Since 2.Bxd5 is stalemate.) **2.Bh7 Bf7! 3.Bg6** (3.g6 Bxg6! draws–note White's Bishop is the "wrong-color" to Queen the h-pawn after 4.Bxg6.) **3...Ba2 4.Bf5** (4.Be8 Bf7 5.Bd7 Be6! 6.Bc6 Bd5 and the stalemate defense allows Black to pursue the Bishop endlessly.) **4...Be6 5.Kg6 Bf7+ 6.Kf6 Bxh5 7.Be6 Bg6!** (Again, stalemate occurs on 8.Kxg6.) **8.Bf7 Bd3 9.Bg6 Bc4 10.Bf5 Bf7!** drawing, as White has no way to make progress.

186) 1...f6 2.Kc5 Bd7 (Black simply waits, daring White to make progress.) **3.Bg8 h6 4.Kd5 Ba4 5.Kd4 Bd7 6.Bc4 Ba4 7.Bd3 Be8 8.h4 g5** (Black is happy to trade off pawns–a good general principle for the weaker side in many types of endings.) **9.exf6+ Kxf6 10.fxg5+ hxg5 11.Be4 gxh4 12.gxh4** and it's a standard drawing position. Black's King heads for h8.

187) 1.Bg7 Ba7 (1...Bc7 2.h6 Kg8 3.Bf8!! Bb6 [3...Kxf8 4.h7 wins] 4.Kd3 [stopping 4...Bd4] 4...Bf2 5.f7+! Kxf7 [5...Kh7 6.Bxd6 and 7.f8=Q] 6.h7 wins.) **2.h6 Kg6** (2...Kg8 amounts to the same thing.) **3.Bh8!!** (Since 3....Kxh6 4.f7 wins.) **3...Bf2** (3...Bd4 4.f7!) **4.h7 Bh4 5.f7 Bg5+** (5...Be7 6.Bf6!! wins.) **6.Kd3 Bh6 7.Bg7!! Kxg7 8.f8=Q+ Kxf8 9.h8=Q+** winning.

188) 1.c7 (Threatening 2.c8=Q+ Bxc8 3.g8=Q+ or 2.g8=Q+ Bxg8 3.c8=Q+.) **1...Kd7** (1...Bd7+ 2.Bc6! wins.) **2.Bf5! Kxc7 3.Bxe6 c2 4.g8=Q c1=Q 5.Qc8+** winning Black's Queen.

189) 1...Bh4! (Threatening 2...Bxg3! 3.hxg3 h2.) **2.gxh4 g3! 3.hxg3 h2** and Queens.

190) 1.a6! Be8 2.g4! (Threatening 3.Bg2 which would allow the a-pawn to run to a8.) **2...Bc6 3.Bg2!! Bxg2 4.e4! f5 5.gxf5 exf5 6.a7 fxe4 7.d4!** (Not 7.a8=Q exd3+ and 8...Bxa8.) **7...e3 8.dxe5 Kb5 9.e6 Kb6** (9...Kc6 10.a8=Q+.) **10.e7 Bc6 11.e8=Q Bxe8 12.a8=Q** winning.

191) 1.Bd6+ Kf7 2.Bc5 (Stopping 2...e2.) **2...Ke6 3.Bd4 Be1 4.Bxe3 Bd2 5.Bg5 Kf5** (It looks bad for White now.) **6.f4 Bxf4** (Expecting 7.Bxf4 Kxf4 8.Kg6 Ke3 and 9...Kd2 winning.) **7.Kh5!** drawing since 7...Bxg5 stalemates and 7...Be5 8.Bc1 gets nothing either.

192) 1.Be4! Bg8 (Forced.) **2.d5+ Kf6** (Or 2...Kd6 3.Ka5 Kc7 4.Ka6 Kb8 5.d6 with an easy win.) **3.d6 Be6** (3...Ke6 4.Bd5+! Kxd5 5.d7 wins.) **4.Bf5!! Kxf5 5.g8=Q Bxg8 6.d7** winning.

193) 1.Ba7! (Since 1...Bxa7 2.h7 wins.) **1...Ba1 2.Kb1 Bc3 3.Kc2 Ba1 4.Bd4!!** (Since 4...exd4 5.Kd3 and h7-h8=Q.) **4...Bxd4 5.Kd3 Ba1 6.Ke4!** and h7-h8=Q is assured.

194) 1...Bxh6! simple and convincing as 2.Kxh6 is stalemate and otherwise it is a draw since with opposite colored Bishop's the g-pawn can never cross g7.

195) 1.Bb5+ (Not 1.Bg4+ Kc7 2.Ke4 Bf2 3.d6+ Kc6 draws.) **1...Ke7** (On 1...Kc7 2.Ke4 Bf2 3.d6+ and 4.c6 wins, or 2...Bh2 3.Kf5 Bg3 4.Ke6 and 5.d6+ wins.) **2.Ba4 Bf4 3.Kc4** (Maneuvering in order to help his pawns advance. Of course not 3.d6+ Bxd6 4.cxd6+ Kxd6 drawing.) **3...Bg3 4.Kb5 Kd7 5.Kb6+ Ke7 6.Kc6 Bf4 7.d6+ Ke6 8.Bb3+ Ke5 9.Kd7 Kd4 10.c6** and c7-c8=Q winning.

196) 1.Kb4 (1.Ba5+ Kd7 [1...Kb7? 2.Kd4 followed by 3.Ke5, 4.Kd6 and 5.c6+ with a direct win] 2.Bb6 Bg2 3.Kb4 Bf3 4.Ka5 Bb7! [stopping 5.Ka6] 5.Ba7 [hoping for 6.Kb6] 5...Kc7! stopping Kb6, and Black draws.) **1...Bg2 2.Ka5** (Threatening 3.Ka6 and if 2...Bb7 then 3.Bf4+ and 4.Kb6 winning.) **2...Kb7 3.Bg5 Bf3 4.Bd8 Bg2 5.Bb6** (Or 5.Kb4–trying to maneuver his King to d6 via the e5 square–but then 5...Kc8! 6.Ba5 Kd7! forestalls that plan.) **5...Bf3 6.Kb4 Bh5! 7.Ba5 Be8!** drawing, as the White King is tied down to the defense of the b5 pawn.

ROOK AND PAWN ENDINGS

Rook and pawn endings are both the most common and most technically challenging of all basic endgames. A thorough mastery of these endings is held by only a very few strong Grandmasters. Don't let this discourage you, for the more you learn about Rook and pawn endings, the quicker you will surpass those who have failed to do their homework!

Many of the following examples will enthrall you with their beauty and intricacies. As always, we provide you with general hints or suggestions, but most of the work will be your challenge. Do not worry if some of these problems seem too difficult! Rook and pawn endings are hard for every chessplayer. Follow the solution to the end and then work backwards if necessary. This retrograde method will give you a better feel for the subtleties involved.

Pay particular attention to No.235 (Lucena's position) and No.236 (Philidor's position). These examples are cornerstones of Rook and pawn endings. You *must know* them in order to properly handle many of the other Rook and pawn positions.

W   + -

No.197
HINT: The Black pawn is not far enough advanced to draw against White's King and Rook.

MODERATE

B   =

No.198
HINT: With the option to move forward two squares, the h-pawn leaps to the 5th rank. This, coupled with the fairly advanced position of the Black King, allows the draw.

EASY

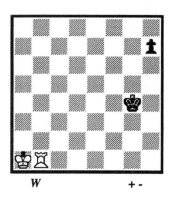

W   + -

No.199
HINT: This position is identical to No.198; however, with White moving first, he wins.

MODERATE

B   =

No.200

HINT: With the move, Black can draw by combining stalemate possibilities with a threat to Queen the pawn.

EASY

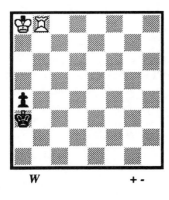

W   + -

No.201

HINT: This is identical to No.200; but, with White to move, he wins.

EASY

W   + -

No.202

HINT: With the White King and Rook behind the enemy pawn, White wins if his King is not more than two ranks from the "square" of the pawn.

MODERATE

W   =

No.203

HINT: Black can draw because White's King and Rook interfere with each other at critical junctures.

DIFFICULT

B   =

No.204

HINT: Black draws by a stalemate defense.

MODERATE

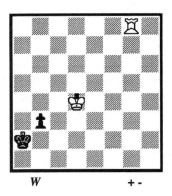

W   + -

No.205

HINT: This is similar to No.204, except that the Rook is in a better position. This allows a win.

MODERATE

W + -

No.206

HINT: White must quickly coordinate his King with the Rook to win.

EASY

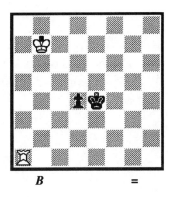

B =

No.207

HINT: With Black to move in the same position, he can draw.

EASY

W + -

No.208

HINT: With the move, White's King can catch Black's pawn.

EASY

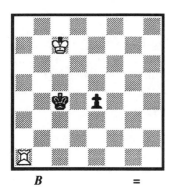

B　　　　　=

No.209

HINT: With the move, Black forces White to sacrifice his Rook for the pawn.

EASY

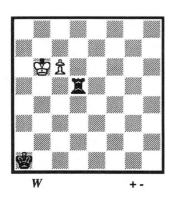

W　　　　　+ -

No.210

HINT: This is a famous position in which the White King and pawn weave a deadly (and beautiful) web of tactics, which eventually win the Rook or mate.

DIFFICULT

W　　　　　+ -

No.211

HINT: With the move, White's King and pawn can coordinate to defeat the Black Rook.

DIFFICULT

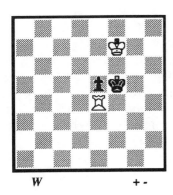

W   + -

No.212
HINT: White must find subtle Rook moves to allow his King to come into play to stop the pawn.

DIFFICULT

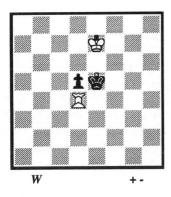

W   + -

No.213
HINT: White wins by proper waiting moves, placing Black into *zugzwang* and winning. Note the similarity of this to No.212.

DIFFICULT

B   =

No.214
HINT: The Black King draws by approaching his pawn while "shielding-out" the White King.

MODERATE

B   + -

No.215

HINT: If the Kings are distant, two connected passers on the 6th rank normally win against a Rook (However, there are some exceptional positions–which we will test you with in other examples).

EASY

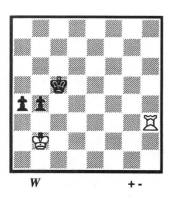

W   + -

No.216

HINT: White maneuvers to force the advance of the connected passers, then he blockades and destroys them (The classic Nimzowitsch procedure–see the monumental treatise *My System-21st Century Edition*, Hays Publishing, 1991.)

EASY

B   - +

No.217

HINT: With the move, Black is able to blockade White's passers and then win them.

EASY

B　　　　　=

No.218
HINT: With far advanced f- and g-pawns (Or b- and c- pawns.) there is sometimes the possibility of a stalemate defense.

DIFFICULT

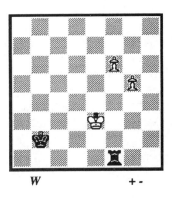

W　　　　　+ -

No.219
HINT: White's King helps support the pawns while finessing the Black King out of position at a critical juncture.

DIFFICULT

B　　　　　=

No.220
HINT: Black's position looks hopeless, but hidden tactical resources save the draw.

DIFFICULT

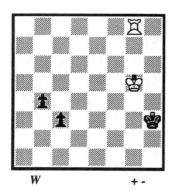

W + -

No.221
HINT: A well-timed Rook check allows White to eventually win Black's pawns.

DIFFICULT

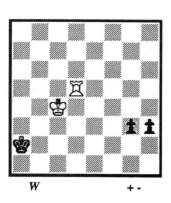

W + -

No.222
HINT: Normally two connected passers on the 6th rank (Or the 3rd rank from Black's viewpoint.) win against a Rook–assuming the Kings are not too close. However, in this case some subtle tactics turn the tables for a White win.

DIFFICULT

W + -

No.223
HINT: White can win by setting up a discovered check.

DIFFICULT

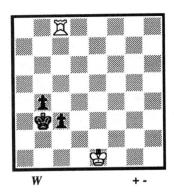

W   + -

No.224
HINT: Tactical motifs allow White's King to cooperate with the Rook, winning.

MODERATE

W   =

No.225
HINT: White's King and Rook seem too far away to cope with the Black duo on the 3rd rank. Tactics make it possible to hold the draw.

DIFFICULT

B   - +

No.226
HINT: Black to move can win, but the wrong first move can allow a draw. See next example for the same position with White to move.

MODERATE

W   =

No.227
HINT: White's King can move to cooperate with his pawns, drawing.

MODERATE

W   + -

No.228
HINT: Three connected pawns on the 5th rank, with the Kings far away, should win.

EASY

B   =

No.229
HINT: Three connected pawns arrayed on the 5th, 4th and 3rd ranks usually draw.

DIFFICULT

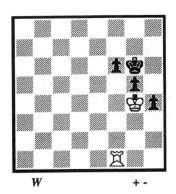

W   + -

No.230
HINT: Three connected pawns arrayed on the 6th, 5th and 4th ranks usually lose if the enemy King is in front of them.

MODERATE

B   - +

No.231
HINT: Three connected pawns on the 4th, 3rd and 2nd ranks often can win.

EASY

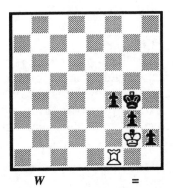

W   =

No.232
HINT: This is the same position as No.231, but with the move White can draw by a stalemate defense.

MODERATE

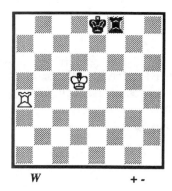

W   + -

No.233
HINT: White wins by an unanswerable first move.

EASY

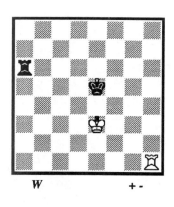

W   + -

No.234
HINT: White can win Black's Rook.

EASY

W   + -

No.235
HINT: This position is of paramount importance for Rook and pawn endings. It is known as Lucena's position and was discovered around 500 years ago!

DIFFICULT

B   =

No.236
HINT: Along with Lucena's position (Seen in No.235.), this position–known as Philidor's position–is of great theoretical importance.

DIFFICULT

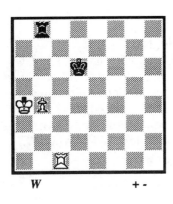

W   + -

No.237
HINT: As a general rule, with the enemy King cut off by a file by the opposing Rook, and the pawn is able to immediately reach the 5th rank–it's a win.

MODERATE

B   =

No.238
HINT: With the move, Black draws by confining the White King.

MODERATE

B   =

No.239
HINT: White's Rook is poorly placed in front of its pawn. This plus the particular positions of the Kings lead to a draw.

MODERATE

B   =

No.240
HINT: With an a- or h-pawn on the 7th rank, and its Rook in front of it, the defending King should ideally be placed on g7 or h7 (This is the case of the a-pawn. For the h-pawn it would be b7 or a7.)

EASY

B   =

No.241
HINT: Black's Rook is best placed behind the enemy pawn–say on a1 or a2. Here it is less favorably placed, but he can just draw with accurate play.

DIFFICULT

B   =

No.242
HINT: Black draws with timely checks and waiting moves.

MODERATE

W   + -

No.243
HINT: White plans to drive back the Black King to facilitate the Queening of the pawn.

MODERATE

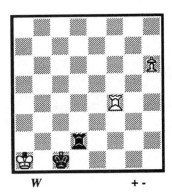

W   + -

No.244
HINT: A neat tactical twist allows the h-pawn to Queen.

MODERATE

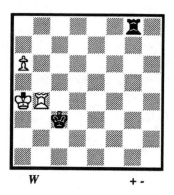

W   + -

No.245
HINT: With an a- or h-pawn, there are winning chances if the pawn is on the 6th rank and the stronger side's Rook is on the adjacent file.

EASY

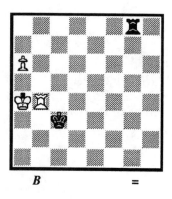

B   =

No.246
HINT: With the move Black barely draws against the pawn on the 6th rank–an exception to the general rule.

EASY

B   =

No.247
HINT: Black to move draws, as an a- or h- pawn usually only draws if the pawn is on the 5th rank.

MODERATE

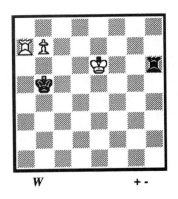

W   + -

No.248
HINT: A subtle White King move allows a winning *zugzwang*.

DIFFICULT

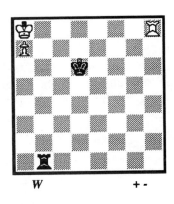

W   + -

No.249
HINT: With White to move, he wins by freeing his King from the corner.

MODERATE

B   =

No.250
HINT: Black to move can draw by checking the White King repeatedly, preventing White from making progress.

MODERATE

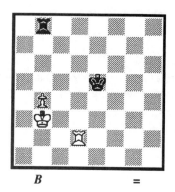

B   =

No.251
HINT: Black holds the draw with astute King maneuvering.

DIFFICULT

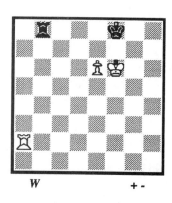

W   + -

No.252
HINT: Black's Rook is tied to the back rank due to mating threats, enabling White to win with Rook maneuvers.

EASY

B   + -

No.253
HINT: Black's King must move (Due to the threat of Rh8#.), then White's King can assist the pawn's advance.

MODERATE

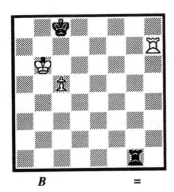

B   **=**

No.254
HINT: Black must find a key concept, moving his King in the proper direction to be on the "right" side of the pawn at critical moments.

DIFFICULT

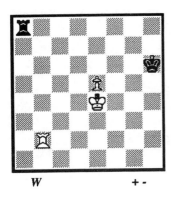

W   **+ -**

No.255
HINT: White wins by eventually transposing into Lucena's position.

MODERATE

W   **+ -**

No.256
HINT: With an a- or b-pawn (Or g- or h-pawn.) on the 3rd or 4th rank (With its King nearby.), it's a win only if the enemy King is cordoned off three files from the pawn.

DIFFICULT

B =

No.257
HINT: With the move, Black can move his King to within two files of the pawn, which allows a theoretical draw.

DIFFICULT

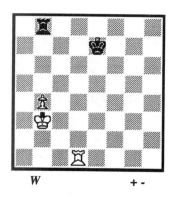

W + -

No.258
HINT: With White to move he wins as Black's King isn't able to attack White's Rook at a crucial moment.

MODERATE

B =

No.259
HINT: Black to play can draw by preventing White's Rook from occupying d6.

MODERATE

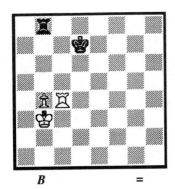

B   =

No.260
HINT: Black to move can utilize his King to harass the White Rook at critical moments.

DIFFICULT

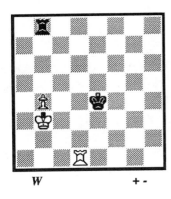

W   + -

No.261
HINT: With the move White can control the 6th rank, which eventually leads to a Lucena's position.

DIFFICULT

W   + -

No.262
HINT: White uses lateral checks to improve his Rook position, which will help shield his King from enemy Rook checks.

DIFFICULT

W   + -

No.263

HINT: This is very similar to Lucena's position. However, since Black's Rook is not on d2, hemming in the White King (As would be the case in Lucena's position.), the win is rather straightforward.

EASY

B   =

No.264

HINT: With the move, Black can check laterally with the Rook, achieving a draw.

EASY

B   =

No.265

HINT: Black draws by arranging to check from the "long side" of the pawn.

DIFFICULT

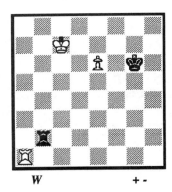

W   + -

No.266
HINT: White wins because Black's King is not on the "ideal" square g7.

MODERATE

W   + -

No.267
HINT: Correct Rook maneuvers allow White to Queen.

MODERATE

B   =

No.268
HINT: This is identical to example No.267, but with Black to move. This allows Black to draw by setting up lateral checks with the Rook.

MODERATE

W   + -

No.269

HINT: White wins because the Black King is on the "long side" of the pawn, which adversely affects his Rook's lateral checking powers.

MODERATE

B   =

No.270

HINT: Black can draw even with his King on the "long side" of the pawn, since the pawn is not yet on the 6th rank.

MODERATE

W   + -

No.271

HINT: White wins by finessing his pawn to the 6th rank.

DIFFICULT

B =

No.272
HINT: With the move Black can draw by alternating threats to check laterally with positioning the Rook to check vertically.

DIFFICULT

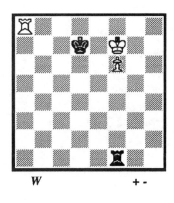

W + -

No.273
HINT: White wins by reaching a Lucena position.

MODERATE

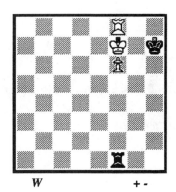

W + -

No.274
HINT: This is an exception to the principle stated in the solution to example No.264.

MODERATE

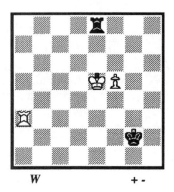

W   + -

No.275
HINT: Black loses because his King is cut off on the 3rd rank *and* White's pawn has reached the 5th rank.

MODERATE

B   =

No.276
HINT: With the move, and as White's pawn is not yet on the 5th rank, Black can draw as his King can cross the 3rd rank.

EASY

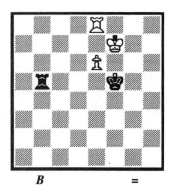

B   =

No.277
HINT: Black to move can draw by some alert tactical play.

DIFFICULT

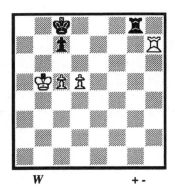

W   + -

No.278
HINT: White can win with direct means, but one obvious choice will allow Black to draw.

EASY

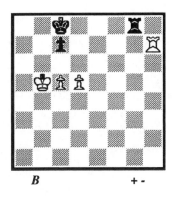

B   + -

No.279
HINT: Even with the move Black loses since his King and Rook are passively placed.

DIFFICULT

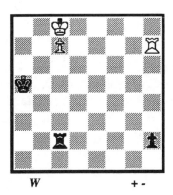

W   + -

No.280
HINT: White's King "stairsteps" down the board to setup a tactic which will Queen the pawn.

DIFFICULT

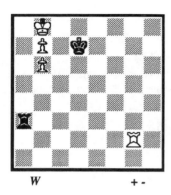

W   + -

No.281

HINT: White uses a brilliant tactical concept to force Black's King to shield the White King from a Black Rook check, thus Queening a pawn.

DIFFICULT

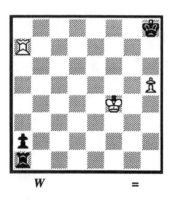

W   =

No.282

HINT: White saves a hopeless looking position. Black threatens to check with the Rook and then Queen, but there is a way out.

DIFFICULT

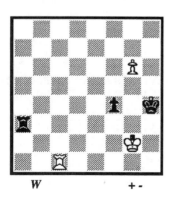

W   + -

No.283

HINT: A subtle first move from White prepares some entertaining tactics.

DIFFICULT

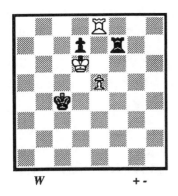

W   + -

No.284

HINT: White snares the Black Rook with a simple but sneaky tactic.

MODERATE

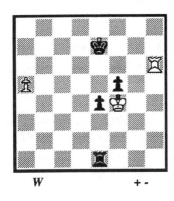

W   + -

No.285

HINT: Both sides Queen, but White's attack comes first.

MODERATE

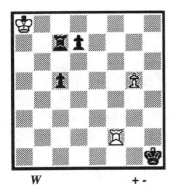

W   + -

No.286

HINT: White, even though a pawn down, exploits the initial move to force his pawn in first.

DIFFICULT

SOLUTIONS FOR EXAMPLES 197-286)

197) 1.Rh5! (Restricting Black's King.) **1...a5 2.Kf7 a4 3.Ke6 a3 4.Rh3! a2 5.Ra3** winning. NOTE: To have a chance to draw, the Black King and pawn must be on at least the 5th rank.

198) 1...h5 2.Kb2 h4 3.Kc2 h3 4.Kd2 h2 5.Ke2 Kg3 (In the nick of time.) **6.Rb3+ Kg2 7.Rb1 h1=Q 8.Rxh1** draw.

199) 1.Rg1+! (A finesse to drive back the Black King. Now on 1...Kf4/f3/h3 or h4 White wins the h-pawn with 2.Rh1.) **1...Kf5 2.Rh1 Kg6 3.Kb2 h5 4.Kc3 Kg5 5.Kd2 h4 6.Ke2 Kg4 7.Kf2 h3 8.Ra1 Kf4 9.Ra4+ Kg5 10.Kg3** wins.

200) 1...Ka2 2.Ka7 a3 3.Ka6 Ka1 4.Ka5 a2 (White must now avoid stalemate.) **5.Kb4 Kb2 6.Kc4+ Kc2** (Or 6...Ka3.) **7.Ra8 Kb2 8.Rb8+ Kc2** with a draw by repetition of moves.

201) 1.Ka7 Ka2 2.Ka6 a3 3.Ka5 Ka1 4.Ka4 a2 (Now it's stalemate if White does nothing to shield the b-file.) **5.Kb3 Kb1 6.Ka3+ Ka1 7.Rh8 Kb1 8.Rh1+ Kc2 9.Kxa2** winning.

202) 1.Kd6 (Simpler [but less instructive than the "hard" way"] is 1.Rf8+ Ke4 2.Kf6 g4 3.Kg5 g3 4.Kh4 g2 5.Rg8 Kf3 6.Kh3 winning the pawn.) **1...g4 2.Kd5 Kf4 3.Kd4 Kf3** (3...g3 4.Rf8+ Kg4 5.Ke3.) **4.Kd3 g3** (4...Kf2 5.Rf8+ Kg2 6.Ke2 Kh2 7.Rg8 g3 8.Kf3.) **5.Rf8+ Kg2 6.Ke2 Kg1** (6...Kh2 7.Rg8 g2 8.Kf2 Kh1 9.Rh8#.) **7.Kf3** (Or 7.Rg8.) **7...g2 8.Rg8 Kh1 9.Kf2!** (Avoiding 9.Rxg2 stalemate.) and wins.

203) We break the solution into three parts:
- a) **1.Rf6+ Ke4 2.Rg6 Kf4 3.Kf6** (Or 3.Ke6 g4 4.Kd5 g3 5.Kd4 Kf3 6.Kd3 g2 7.Kd2 Kf2 8.Rf6+ Kg3 9.Rg6+ Kf2 =) **3...g4 4.Rg8**. The Rg6 blocks 4.Kg6, which is a winning move with the Rook on g8.) **4...g3 5.Kg6 g2 6.Kh5 Kf3 7.Kh4 Kf2** draws.
- b) **1.Kd6** (After 1.Kf7 g4 2.Kg7 g3 3.Kh6 Kf4 4.Kh5 g2 5.Rg6 Kf3 6.Kh4 Kf2 draws.) **1...g4 2.Kd5 g3 3.Kd4 g2! 4.Ra1** (NOTE: 4.Rg6 is impossible–this shows the bad position of the Ra6.) **4...Kf4 5.Kd3 Kf3 6.Kd2 Kf2** draws.
- c) **1.Ra5+ Kf4 2.Kf6 g4 3.Ra4+ Kf3 4.Kf5 g3 5.Ra3+ Kf2 6.Kf4 g2 7.Ra2+ Kf1 8.Kf3** (It looks bad for Black since 8...g1=Q fails to 9.Ra1#.) **8...g1=N+!** with a theoretically drawn ending–see the chapter on Rook and Minor Pieces.

204) 1...b2 2.Rg2 (On 2.Rg8, hoping for 2...b1=Q 3.Ra8#- Black plays 2...b1=N+! with a theoretical draw. See the chapter on Rook and Minor Pieces.) **2...Ka1!** draws as 3.Rxb2 is stalemate.

205) 1.Kc3 b2 2.Ra8+ Kb1 3.Rb8 Ka1 4.Kc2! (Not 4.Rxb2?? stalemate.) and the pawn falls with mate soon to follow.

206) 1.Kc6 d3 2.Kc5 Ke3 3.Kc4 d2 4.Kc3 Ke2 5.Kc2 winning.

207) 1...d3 2.Kc6 d2 3.Kc5 Ke3 4.Kc4 Ke2 5.Ra2 Ke1 6.Ra1+ d1=Q 7.Rxd1+ draw.

208) 1.Kd6 e3 (1...Kd4 2.Ke6 e3 3.Kf5 e2 4.Kf4 Kd3 5.Kf3 Kd2 6.Kf2 wins for White.) **2.Ke5 e2 3.Ke4 Kc3 4.Ke3** winning.

209) 1...e3 2.Kd6 e2 3.Ke5 Kd3 4.Kf4 Kd2 5.Ra2+ Kd3 (Also good is 5...Kd1.) **6.Ra1 Kd2** and draws.

210) 1.c7 Rd6+ 2.Kb5 Rd5+ 3.Kb4 Rd4+ 4.Kb3 Rd3+ 5.Kc2! (It looks like White wins easily, but Black has a cute resource.) **5...Rd4!** (Now 6.c8=Q allows 6...Rc4+! stalemating after 7.Qxc4.) **6.c8=R! Ra4** (The only way to stop Ra8#.) **7.Kb3!** winning, as there is no defense to the dual threats of 8.Rc1# and 8.Kxa4.

211) 1.f7 Rc6+ (Forced.) **2.Ke5!** (Not 2.Ke7? Rc1! 3.f8=Q Re1+ 4.Kf7 Rf1+ drawing.) **2...Rc5+ 3.Ke4 Rc4+ 4.Ke3 Rc3+ 5.Kf2!** (Switching to the g-file.) **5...Rc2+ 6.Kg3 Rc3+ 7.Kg4 Rc4+ 8.Kg5 Rc5+ 9.Kg6 Rc6+ 10.Kg7** winning, as 11.f8=Q can't be stopped.

212) 1.Re2!! (Also good is 1.Re3!!. However, the obvious 1.Re1 allows Black to draw with 1...e4 2.Ke7 Ke5! [keeping the White King at bay] 3.Kd7 Kd5!, or 3.Kf7 Kf5! and White can make no progress as his King is shut-off.) **1...e4** (On 1...Kf4 2.Re1! e4 3.Ke6 White's King comes into play, winning.) **2.Re1!** (A temporizing move, in order to place Black in *zugzwang*.) **2...Ke5 3.Ke7!** (Now Black is in *zugzwang*. Note that White is using the opposition here.) **3...Kd4** (Or 3...Kf4 4.Kd6 e3 5.Kd5 Kf3 6.Kd4 e2 7.Kd3 winning.) **4.Kf6 e3 5.Kf5 Kd3 6.Kf4 e2 7.Kf3** wins.

213) 1.Rd2!! (A key waiting move. Also winning is 1.Rd3!!) **1...d4** (On 1...Ke4 2.Kd6 d4 3.Kc5 d3 4.Kc4 White wins.) **2.Rd1!** (Another waiting move. The point is White will be able to gain the opposition next move, enabling his King to move up and cooperate with the Rook.) **2...Kd5 3.Kd7!**

(Not 3.Kf6 Ke4 4.Ke6 d3 and Black has the opposition, drawing. For example, 5.Kd6 Ke3 6.Kc5 Ke2 7.Ra1 d2 8.Ra2 Ke1, etc.) **3...Ke4 4.Kc6 d3 5.Kc5 Ke3 6.Kc4 d2 7.Kc3** winning.

214) 1...Kd4 (Moving forward to help support his pawn, while keeping the White King away.) **2.Rd1+** (On 2.Kb4 f3 draws,e.g., 3.Kb3 Kd3 4.Ra2 Ke3 5.Kc3 f2 6.Ra1 Ke2 drawing.) **2...Ke3 3.Re1+** (3.Kc4 f3 4.Kc3 f2 5.Kc2 Ke2 6.Rd2+ Ke1 7.Rd1+ Ke2 draws.) **3...Kd2!** (Not 3...Kf2? 4.Re7 f3 5.Kc4 Kg2 6.Kd3 f2 7.Rg7+ Kf3 8.Rf7+ Kg2 9.Ke2 winning for White.) **4.Rf1 Ke3 5.Kc4 f3 6.Kc3 Ke2 7.Rh1 f2 8.Rh2 Ke1** and White must give up his Rook for the pawn, with a draw.

215) 1...Rg5 (1...Rb8 2.g7 [or 2.h7 and 3.g7] 2...Rg8 3.h7 Rxg7 4.h8=Q wins.) **2.g7 Rg6 3.h7 Rxg7 4.h8=Q** winning.

216) 1.Rh4 (Or 1.Kc2. There are various paths to victory here.) **1...Kb5 2.Kc2 Ka5** (2...b3+ 3.Kb2 Ka5 4.Ka3 wins.) **3.Kd3 a3** (3...Kb5 4.Rh5+ Kb6 5.Kc4 b3 6.Kb4 b2 7.Rb5+ Ka6 8.Kxa4 wins.) **4.Kc2** (Or 4.Kc4 Ka4 5.Rh8!) **4...Ka4 5.Rg4 Kb5 6.Kb3 Ka5 7.Rxb4 a2 8.Ra4+** winning.

217) 1...Ke7 2.Kb6 Kd6 3.Kb7 Rg8 4.Kb6 (On 4.d8=Q+ Rxd8 5.c7 Rd7 pins and wins.) **4...Rb8+ 5.Ka7 Kc7 6.Ka6 Kxc6** winning.

218) 1...Ke7 2.Kh6 Kf6 3.Kh7 Rb8 (Expecting 4.g7 Kxf7 or 4.Kh6 Rh8#.) **4.f8=Q+!! Rxf8 5.g7 Rf7 6.Kh8** drawing, as 6...Rxg7 stalemates.

219) 1.Kd4! (Moving up to help his pawns while restricting Black's King.) **1...Kb3** (1...Rf5 2.Ke4! Rxg5 3.f7 Rg4+ 4.Ke3 Rg3+ 5.Kf2 Queens.) **2.Ke5 Kc4 3.g6 Re1+ 4.Kd6 Rg1 5.g7!!** (Not 5.f7 Rxg6+ 6.Ke5 Rg5+ 7.Kf6 Rg1 8.f8=Q Rf1+ drawing. Also, if 7.Ke4 [instead of 7.Kf6] then 7...Rg1! and now 8.f8=Q? loses to 8...Re1+ 9.Kf5 Rf1+ and 10...Rxf8.) **5...Kd4! 6.Kc6!!** (The only way to win. After 6.f7 Rg6+ 7.Ke7 Rxg7 Black draws; also, 6.Ke6 Ke4 7.Kf7 Kf5 draws for Black.) **6...Kc4!** (In order to force a pin–as in the last note–after 7.f7 Rg6+ 8.Kd7 Rxg7 which draws easily.) **7.Kd7!** (Heading for e8.) **7...Kd5 8.Ke8 Ke6 9.f7 Ra1** (Since 10.f8=Q or 10.g8=Q allows 10...Ra8#.) **10.f8=N+! Kf6 11.g8=Q** wins.

220) 1...Kc3! (Threatening mate–this will be the drawing theme.) **2.Kb1 Ra6! 3.b7** (Forced 3.Kc1 Ra1#.) **3...Rb6+ 4.Kc1** (4.Ka1 Ra6+ gets White nowhere.) **4...Rh6! 5.Kd1 Kd3! 6.Ke1 Ke3 7.Kf1 Kf3 8.Kg1 Rg6+ 9.Kf1** (9.Kh1 Rh6+.) **9...Rh6 10.Ke1 Ke3** and Black draws by perpetual mate threats.

221) 1.Kf4! (Not 1.Rc8? Kg3 2.Rc4 Kf3 3.Rxb4 Ke3 4.Rc4 Kd2 draws.)
1...c2 (1...b3? 2.Rg3+ and 3.Rxc3.) **2.Rh8+! Kg2 3.Rc8 b3 4.Ke3 Kf1** (Note
4...b2 allows 5.Rxc2 with check, this is possible because of 2.Rh8+!) **5.Kd2
Kf2 6.Rb8** winning the pawns.

222) 1.Rd2+ Kb1 (Not 1...Ka3 2.Rd3+ and 3.Rxg3, while 1...Ka1??
allows mate after 2.Kb3 and 3.Rd1.) **2.Kc3! Kc1** (2...g2 3.Rd1+ Ka2
4.Rg1! wins– e.g., 4...Ka3 5.Ra1#, or 4...h2 5.Rxg2+.) **3.Ra2 Kb1** (3...Kd1
4.Kd3 Kc1 [4...Ke1 5.Ke3 Kf1 6.Kf3 and 7.Kxg3 wins] 5.Ke3 h2 6.Ra1+
Kb2 7.Rh1 Kc3 8.Kf3 and White wins.) **4.Re2! g2** (4...h2 is no better after
5.Re1+ Ka2 6.Rh1! g2 7.Rxh2.) **5.Re1+ Ka2 6.Rg1! h2** (Forced as 6...Ka3
allows mate.) **7.Rxg2+** wins.

223) 1.Kd2! (The only winning move. 1.Rf1 g2 2.Ke1 only draws.) **1...f2**
(1...g2 2.Ke3.) **2.Rd1! g2** (Or 2...Ke5 3.Ke3 Kf5 4.Kf3 wins the pawns.)
3.Ke2+ winning the pawns by discovered check–made possible by 2.Rd1!.

224) 1.Rb8! (Stopping ...Kb2, which would allow Black to draw.) **1...Ka3**
(1...c2 2.Kd2 Kb2 3.Rxb4+.) **2.Kd1 b3 3.Kc1 Ka4** (3...c2 4.Ra8+ Kb4 5.Kb2
wins.) **4.Rc8** (Preparing to force the pawns to advance, in order to blockade
and destroy them.) **4...Kb4 5.Kb1! b2 6.Kc2 Ka3 7.Rxc3+ Ka2 8.Rb3
Ka1**(A last desperate try as 8...b1=Q+ 9.Rxb1 is totally hopeless.) **9.Ra3#**
but not 9.Rxb2?? stalemate.

225) 1.Rc4+ Kb3 (1...Kb5 2.Rc1 f2 3.Rb1+ Ka4 4.Kc4 Ka3 5.Kc3 Ka4
[5...Ka2? 6.Rf1! wins: 6...Ka3 7.Ra1#, or 6...g2 7.Rxf2+] 6.Kc4 Ka5 7.Kc5
drawing by repetition of moves.) **2.Rf4 f2 3.Kc5! Kc2** (3...g2 4.Rf3+ Ka4
5.Rf4+ Ka5 6.Rf3! with perpetual mating threats, drawing.) **4.Kd4 Kd2
5.Rf3 Ke2 6.Re3+ Kd1 7.Rd3+ Kc1 8.Rc3+ Kb1** (8...Kb2 9.Rf3 draws.)
9.Rb3+ Kc1 (9...Ka2? loses after 10.Rf3 Kb1 11.Ke3 Kc1 12.Ke2 and
13.Rxg3.) **10.Rc3+** and White draws (Or, if Black is careless, wins.) by
perpetual check or by threats we have seen in previous notes above.

226) 1...Rf7 (Or 1...Rh7 winning. White can draw after 1...Ra6? 2.h7! Ra8
3.Kc4 Rd8 4.Kc5 Kc2 5.Kc6 Kd3 6.f7 Ke4 7.Kc7 Rh8 8.Kd6 Kf5 9.Ke7
Rxh7 10.Ke8 Rh8+ 11.f8=Q+ Rxf8+ 12.Kxf8 draw.)

227) 1.Kc4 Rf7 (1...Kc2 2.Kd5 Kd3 3.Ke6 Rh7! [not 3...Ke4? 4.f7 winning]
4.f7 Rxh6+ draws.) **2.h7! Rxh7 3.Kd5 Kc2 4.Ke6 Kd3 5.f7 Rh8 6.Ke7**
drawing.

228) 1.g6 Rxf5 2.h6 Rg5 (2...Rf6 3.g7 or 3.h7 wins.) **3.h7 Rh5 4.g7** winning.

229) 1...Kf6 (Not 1...Kh5 2.Rd2 Kh4? 3.Rd6 Kh5 4.Re6 h2 5.Re8 and 6.Rh8 winning.) **2.Re2 Kf7! 3.Re5** (3.Kxf5 g3! wins for Black.) **3...Kg6 4.Re6+** (Not 4.Rxf5? h2! 5.Rg5+ Kh6 wins for Black.) **4...Kg7** (4...Kh7 5.Kg5! Kg7 6.Rg6+ Kh7 7.Rh6+ Kg7 8.Rh5 Kf7 9.Kxf5 wins, or 4...Kh5 5.Rd6! h2 6.Rd8 wins the h-pawn.) **5.Rd6** (Or 5.Kg5 h2 6.Re7+ Kf8 7.Rh7 g3 8.Kf6 Kg8 9.Rh3 f4 10.Rh5 f3 11.Rg5+ Kf8 12.Rh5 Ke8 13.Ke6 Kd8 14.Kd6, etc. The perpetual mating threats allow White to draw.) **5...Kf7 6.Rh6 Kg7 7.Rh5** (7.Kg5 f4! 8.Kxg4 Kxh6 9.Kxh3 draws.) **7...Kg6 8.Rg5+ Kh6! 9.Rg8** (Not 9.Kxf5 h2, or 9.Rxf5 h2 and Black wins.) **9...Kh7 10.Rd8 Kg6** and White can make no progress–it's a draw.

230) 1.Rf2 Kg7 2.Kf5 Kf7 3.Re2 Kg7 4.Re6 Kh7 (4...h3 5.Re3 h2 6.Rh3 wins.) **5.Rxf6 h3 6.Kxg5 h2 7.Rh6+** wins.

231) 1...f3+ 2.Rxf3 h1=Q+ 3.Kxh1 Kxf3 4.Kg1 g2 5.Kh2 Kf2 winning.

232) 1.Kh1! f3 (1...Kh3 2.Rf3! holds.) **2.Rxf3** draws since 2...Kxf3 stalemates. This drawing method would not work if the pawns were shifted a file to the left.

233) 1.Ke6! and Black must resign as 2.Ra8# is threatened and 1...Kd8 2.Ra8+ Kc7 3.Rxf8 wins.

234) 1.Rh5+ Kd6 (Or e6 or f6.) **2.Rh6+** and **3.Rxa6** wins.

235) 1.Re1+ Kd7 (On 1...Kf6 2.Kf8 and 3.g8=Q wins; also, 1...Kd6 2.Kf8 Rf2+ 3.Ke8 Rg2 4.Re7 Rg1 5.Kf8 Rf1+ 6.Rf7 wins.) **2.Re4!** (This move prepares to "build a bridge", a term referring to the technique of allowing the White King to "walk over" to a position allowing the pawn to Queen. The Rook will later shield the King from checks.) **2...Rh1** (Or 2...Rf2 3.Rh4 [3.Kh7 also wins] 3...Rf1 4.Kh8 wins.) **3.Kf7** (Now the King can come out.) **3...Rf1+ 4.Kg6 Rg1+ 5.Kf6 Rf1+** (5...Kd6 6.Rd4+ Kc6 [6...Kc7 7.Rd5 followed by Rg5 wins] 7.Rd8 Rf1+ 8.Ke5 Re1+ 9.Kf4 Rf1+ 10.Ke3 Re1+ 11.Kf2 wins.) **6.Kg5 Rg1+ 7.Rg4** (Now the "bridge" is seen.) and Black must resign. NOTE: You *must know* this position well, as it is fundamental to a large number of Rook and pawn endings.

236) 1...Ra6! (This is a fundamental idea in Philidor's position. Black's Rook moves to the 6th rank in order to stop the enemy King from advancing to the 6th rank.) **2.Rb7 Rc6!** (The Rook must watch the 6th rank–until White advances the pawn. Then Black will immediately move his Rook to the 1st rank in order to check White's King from behind and thus frustrate any attempts to win.) **3.Ra7 Rb6 4.e6 Rb1! 5.Kf6 Rf1+ 6.Ke5 Re1+ 7.Kd6 Rd1+** and White is getting nowhere. You *must know* this defensive method to play Rook and pawn endings well.

237) 1.b5 Kd7 2.Ka5 (Not 2.Kb4? Rc8 3.Rxc8 [otherwise Black's King moves in front of the pawn, drawing] 3...Kxc8 4.Ka5 Kb7 drawing easily.) **2...Ra8+ 3.Kb6 Rb8+ 4.Ka6 Ra8+ 5.Kb7 Ra2 6.b6 Rb2 7.Ka7 Ra2+ 8.Kb8 Rb2 9.b7 Ra2 10.Rc4!**–note that we have transposed into Lucena's position and thus a definite win.

238) 1...Kc7 (Not 1...Kc6? 2.Rc8+ Kd7 3.Rb8 Rc1 4.Kb7 Rb1+ 5.Ka6 Ra1+ 6.Kb6 Rb1+ 7.Kc5 and the a-pawn Queens.) **2.Rb8 Rc1 3.Rb7+ Kc8 4.Rb8+ Kc7** and it's a draw since the White King can't escape from a8.

239) 1...Kf5 (White threatened Rg8+ and a8=Q.) **2.Ke7** (2.Ke8 Ke6 keeps White's King hemmed-in, a key motif in Black's defense.) **2...Ke5 3.Kd7 Kd5 4.Kc7 Kc5 5.Kb7** (5.Rc8 Rxa7+ 6.Kb8+ Kb6 draws.) **5...Rb1+ 6.Ka6 Ra1+ 7.Kb7** and White gets nowhere, draw.

240) 1...Ra2 (Black's defense is simplicity itself: he just waits. A blunder would be 1...Kf7? as then 2.Rh8! wins since 2...Rxa7 3.Rh7+ wins the Rook.) **2.Ke5 Ra1 3.Kd5 Ra2 4.Kc5 Ra1 5.Kb6 Rb1+** (Once the White King protects the pawn, freeing the Rook, Black must check him away.) **6.Kc6 Ra1** and White can't win.

241) 1...Kf6+! (The King must move away from the pawn. The natural looking 1...Kd6+ loses: 2.Kd4 Ke6 [2...Rd7 3.Kc4 Rc7+ 4.Kb5 Rd7 5.Kb6 Kd5 6.Rb8 Queens] 3.Kc5 Ke5 4.Kc6 Re6+ [4...Ke4 5.Kd6 wins, as does 4...Ke6 5.Kb6] 5.Kd7 Rd6+ 6.Kc7 wins.) **2.Kd4 Rf7!** (2...Ke6 3.Kc5 wins; also 2...Rd7+ 3.Kc5 Rf7 4.Kb6 Kf5 5.Rb8 wins.) **3.Kd5** (3.Kc5 Kf5 4.Kb6 Rf6+ 5.Kb7 Rf7+ 6.Ka6 Rf6+ draws.) **3...Kf5 4.Kd6 Kf6** (Not 4...Rf6+? 5.Ke7 Re6+ 6.Kd7 and Black loses.) **5.Kc6 Kf5 6.Kc5 Kf4!** (Forced. After 6...Kf6 7.Kb6 wins as Black has no good checks.) **7.Kb6 Rf6+ 8.Kc7 Rf7+ 9.Kc6 Kf5!** and White can't make any progress.

242) 1...Rf5+ (Since the a-pawn is defended by its King, White's Rook threatens to move followed by Queening. Therefore, Black bumps the White King with checks.) **2.Kc6 Rf6+ 3.Kd5 Rb6 4.Ke5 Rc6 5.a7 Ra6!** reaching the draw.

243) 1.Kg8 Rg2+ (Forced.) **2.Kf8 Rh2** (Forced.) **3.Rb6+** (The key motif: Black's King is driven back.) **3...Kf5 4.Kg7 Rg2+ 5.Kf7 Rh2 6.Rb5+ Kf4 7.Kg7 Rg2+ 8.Kh6 Rh2+ 9.Rh5** winning.

244) 1.h7 Rd8 (1...Rh2 2.Rf1+ Kd2 3.Rf2+! Rxf2 4.h8=Q.) **2.Rc4+ Kd2 3.Rd4+! Rxd4 4.h8=Q** winning.

245) 1.a7 Ra8 (White threatened 2.Rb8.) **2.Rb7 Kc4 3.Ka5 Kc5 4.Ka6 Kc6 5.Rb8** winning.

246) 1...Rg6 (Not 1...Ra8 2.Rb6) **2.Rb3+** (If 2.Ka5 Rxa6+! draws immediately.) **2...Kc4 3.Rb4+ Kc3 4.Kb5 Rxa6!** with a draw.

247) 1...Rg6+ 2.Ka7 (2.Rb6 Rg5 holds.) **2...Rg7+ 3.Rb7 Rg6!** (Not 3...Rg1 4.a6 Kc5 5.Rc7+ Kb5 [or 5...Kd6 6.Kb8 Ra1 7.a7 Ra2 8.Rb7! and 9.a8=Q, but not 8.a8=Q Rxa8+ 9.Kxa8 Kxc7] 6.Kb7 followed by a7 wins.) **4.a6 Kc5 5.Rb1 Rg7+ 6.Ka8 Kc6** and Black draws as White's King is poorly placed in front of his pawn.

248) 1.Ke5!! (The point will soon be clear.) **1...Rb6 2.Kd5!** (Now Black is in *zugzwang*. Note that 2.Kd5? Rb6 leaves White in *zugzwang*, losing his pawn after 3.Kd4 Kc6.) **2...Kb4 3.Ra1!** (Now 4...Rxb7 loses the Rook to 5.Rb1+.) **3...Kb5 4.Rb1+ Ka6 5.Rxb6+ Kxb6 6.b8=Q+** winning.

249) 1.Rb8 Rc1 2.Kb7 Rb1+ 3.Kc8 Rc1+ 4.Kd8 Rh1 (Threat: 5...Rh8#.) **5.Rb6+ Kc5 6.Rc6+!Kb5** (6...Kxc6 allows 7.a8=Q+.) **7.Rc8** shielding the back rank and winning as a8=Q can't be stopped.

250) 1...Ra8+ (Not 1...Kd7 [in order to oppose Rooks with 2...Rc8] 2.Rc4! [protecting the b-pawn to allow White's King to advance to a6] 2...Ra8+ 3.Kb5 Rb8+ 4.Ka6 Ra8+ 5.Kb7 followed by b5, winning.) **2.Kb3** (2.Kb5 Rb8+ 3.Ka5 Ra8+ 4.Kb6 Rb8+ 5.Ka5 and White gets nowhere.) **2...Kd7** (To oppose Rooks, allowing Black's King to come across.) **3.Rc4 Rc8 4.Rxc8 Kxc8 5.Ka4 Kb8 6.Kb5 Kb7** and Black holds the opposition, drawing easily.

251) 1...Ke6! (Not 1...Ke4? 2.Rd6 [or 2.Rd7] 2...Ke5 3.Ra6 Kd5 4.Ka4 Kc4 [or 4...Rh8 5.b5 Rh1 6.Rc6 winning for White] 5.Rc6+ Kd5 6.b5 winning.) **2.Rd4** (Defending the b-pawn and thus threatening to advance the King in front of the pawn.) **2...Ke5!** (2...Ke7? 3.Kc4 Rc8+ 4.Kb5 Rb8+ 5.Ka6 Ke6 6.b5 winning.) **3.Rd1** (Now the Rook doesn't protect the b-pawn and White's King can't advance.) **3...Ke6 4.Rd2 Ke5** and White can make no progress.

252) 1.Rh2 (Threat: 2.Rh8#.) **1...Kg8 2.Rg2+ Kh8** (2...Kf8 3.e7+ wins.) **3.Kf7 Rb7+ 4.e7** and Black must resign.

253) 1...Kc8 (Or 1...Ke8 2.Rh8+ Kf7 3.Kd7 Ra1 4.d6 Ra7+ 5.Kc6 Ra6+ 6.Kc7 Ra7+ 7.Kb6 Rd7 8.Kc6 Ra7 9.d7 wins.) **2.Rh8+ Kb7 3.Kd7 Rg1 4.d6 Rg7+ 5.Ke6 Rg6+ 6.Ke7 Rg7+** (Or 6...Kc6 7.Rc8+ Kb7 8.d7 winning.) **7.Kf6 Rd7 8.Ke6 Rg7 9.d7** wins.

254) 1...Rc1 (1...Rb1+ 2.Kc6 Kb8! [going to the "short side" of the pawn, i.e., the side of the pawn which has the shorter lateral distance from the pawn to the side of the board. The "long side" of the pawn in this case would be to the right of the pawn.] 3.Rh8+ Ka7 4.Kc7 Rb7+ 5.Kd6 Rg7 6.Rd8 Rg6+ 7.Kc7 Rg7+ 8.Kc8 Rg6 drawing.) **2.Kc6 Kb8!** (The King must go to the "short side" of the pawn. Going to the "long side" loses: 2...Kd8 3.Rh8+ Ke7 4.Rc8! with a winning position.) **3.Rh8+ Ka7 4.Rc8 Rh1!** (Now if 5.Kc7 then 5...Rh7+ 6.Kd6 Rh6+, etc. Note: With the Black King on e7 [as in the previous note after 3...Ke7!] a check on h7 is blocked by his own King.) **5.Rd8** (Planning 6.Kc7 and if 6...Rh7+ then 7.Rd7.) **5...Rc1! 6.Rd5 Kb8 7.Kd7 Kb7** and White is getting nowhere.

255) 1.Rg2! (Keeping Black's King hemmed in.) **1...Re8 2.Kf5 Rf8+ 3.Ke6 Re8+ 4.Kf6 Rf8+ 5.Ke7 Rf1 6.e6** and White cannot be stopped from obtaining Lucena's position.

256) 1.Re1! (Cutting off Black's King.) **1...Kf5** (1...Kf7 2.Re5! Kf6 3.Rc5 Ke6 4.b5 Kd7 5.Kb4 Rc8 6.b6! Rxc5 7.Kxc5 Kd8 [7...Kc8 8.Kc6 wins] 8.Kd6 [not 8.Kc6? Kc8! drawing] 8...Kc8 9.Kc6 Kb8 10.b7 wins.) **2.Kc4 Rc8+ 3.Kd5 Rb8 4.Rb1 Kf6 5.b5 Ke7 6.Kc6 Kd8 7.b6 Kc8 8.Rh1!** wins as 9.Rh8+ is crushing.

257) 1...Ke6! 2.Rd4 Ke5! (A key technique; whenever the strong side's Rook protects its pawn, the defender's King should attack it.) **3.Rd7 Ke6 4.Rd4 Ke5! 5.Kc3 Rh8** (Or 5...Ra8, which also draws.) **6.b5 Rb8 7.Rb4** (Or 7.Rh4 Kd6! [getting in front of the pawn, a basic drawing method] 8.Kb4 Kc7 with a draw.) **7...Kd5!** (Drawing as White can't stop Black's King from getting in front of the pawn–or winning it.) **8.Kb3 Kc5 9.Rc4+ Kb6** (Not 9...Kxb5?? 10.Rb4+.)

258) 1.Rd4 Ke6 2.Kc4 Ke5 (Too late.) **3.Rd5+ Ke6 4.b5 Rc8+ 5.Rc5 Kd7 6.b6! Rxc5+ 7.Kxc5 Kd8** (7...Kc8 8.Kc6 Kb8 9.b7 Ka7 10.Kc7.) **8.Kd6!** (Gaining the opposition.) **8...Kc8 9.Kc6 Kb8 10.b7** winning.

259) 1...Ke5! 2.Rd7 Ke6! (Harassing the Rook is the main drawing motif.) **3.Rd4 Ke5!** and White can't make progress.

260) 1...Kd6! 2.Ka4 (Not 2.Rd4+? Kc6 and the King gets in front of the pawn with a theoretical draw.) **2...Kd5! 3.Rc5+ Kd6 4.Ka5** (4.Rb5 Ra8+ 5.Ra5 Rb8 6.b5 Kc7 draws.) **4...Ra8+ 5.Kb5 Rb8+ 6.Kc4 Rb7** (6...Rh8 is also good.) **7.b5 Rc7! 8.Rxc7 Kxc7** and the King and pawn ending is drawn.

261) 1.Rd6! (We've seen the King cut off on a file in several previous examples; but, cutting the King off on a rank can be equally effective.) **1...Ke5 2.Ra6** (Now White's King can "walk" to a4 without being checked by ...Ra8+.) **2...Kd5 3.Ka4 Rh8** (3...Kc4 4.Rc6+ Kd5 5.b5 Ra8+ 6.Kb4 Ra1 7.Rc8 with a winning position as White can't be stopped from advancing his pawn to the 7th rank with Black's King cut off from getting in front of the pawn–in other words White wins because he will achieve a Lucena's position.) **4.b5 Rh1 5.Rc6 Ra1+ 6.Kb4** transposing into our previous note (Getting Lucena's position.) and thus winning.

262) 1.Rh5+! (Not 1.b4 Rc8+ 2.Kb5 Rb8+ and Black's Rook checking forestalls White's efforts to win.) **1...Ke6 2.Rh6+ Kd7 3.Rh7+ Ke6** (Of course not 3...Kc8?? (Or 3...Kd8??) 4.Rh8+ Kb7 5.Rxb8+ Kxb8 6.Kb6 winning easily.) **4.b4 Rc8+ 5.Kb6 Rb8+ 6.Rb7** (Note the value of 3.Rh7+ here.) **6...Rh8 7.b5 Kd6 8.Rg7 Rb8+ 9.Ka6 Kc5 10.Rc7+ Kd6 11.Rc6+ Kd7 12.Rc1** with a winning position. White will push the pawn to the 7th, achieving Lucena's position.

263) 1.Rg1+! (Driving off the King.) **1...Kh7** (1...Kf6 2.Kf8 and 3.e8=Q.) **2.Re1 Rd2 3.Kf7 Rf2+ 4.Ke6** and Queens.

264) 1...Ra8+ 2.Kd7 Ra7+ 3.Ke6 Ra6+ 4.Ke5 Ra5+ 5.Kd4 Ra4+ 6.Kc5 Ra5+ 7.Kb6 Re5 winning the pawn, drawing. Note: The defender in this and similar situations should strive to check laterally from the "long side" of the pawn–the side more distant from the left or right side of the board.

265) 1...Rb7+ 2.Kd6 Rb6+! (Avoiding 2...Kf8? 3.Ra8+ Kg7 4.e7 winning.) **3.Kd7 Rb7+ 4.Kd8** (4.Kc6 Rb2! 5.Rf1 Re2! 6.Kd7 Ra2! 7.e7 Ra7+ 8.Ke6 Ra6+ drawing.) **4...Rb8+ 5.Kc7 Rb2 6.Rf1** (To stop ...Kf8.) **6...Ra2 7.e7 Ra7+** and again we have our familiar drawing method.

266) 1.Re1! Rc2+ 2.Kd7 Rd2+ 3.Ke8 Ra2 4.e7 and since White threatens both 5.Kf8 and 5.Kd7 followed by Queening, Black cannot defend. Note: With Black's King at g7, 8.Kf8 would not be possible, allowing Black to draw by Rook checks.

267) 1.Rc8 Ra1 (1...Re2 2.Kd7 Rd2+ [2...Kf6 3.Rf8+ Kg7 4.e7 wins] 3.Ke8 Kf6 4.e7 Re2 5.Rc6+ wins.) **2.Ke8 Kf6 3.e7 Ke6 4.Rc6+ Kd5 5.Kd7 Ra8 6.Rc8** winning.

268) 1...Ra1! (Preparing lateral checks.) **2.Rd8 Ra7+ 3.Rd7** (3.Ke8 Kf6 4.Rd6 Re7+ draws.) **3...Ra8 4.Rb7 Kg6!** (Not 4...Kg8 5.Kf6 Kf8 6.Rh7 Kg8 7.Rg7+ Kh8 8.e7 wins.) **5.Kd7** (5.Rc7 Kg7 draws.) **5...Kf6 6.e7** (Or 6.Rc7 Kg7! [not 6...Ra1? 7.e7 Rd1+ 8.Ke8 winning] 7.Kd6+ Kf8 8.Rh7 Ra6+ drawing.) **6...Kf7 7.Rc7 Re8 8.Kd6 Ra8** (Not 8...Rh8? 9.e8=Q+! Kxe8 10.Rc8+.) threatening ...Ra6+ and drawing handily.

269) 1.Rh8 Ra7+ 2.Kc6 Ra6+ 3.Kc7 Ra7+ 4.Kb6 Rd7 5.Kc6 Ra7 (5...Ke6 6.Rh6+ wins.) **6.d7** wins. NOTE: With a pawn on the 6th rank the Black King should be on the "short side" of the pawn to draw.

270) 1...Ra7+ 2.Kb6 Ra1! 3.d6 Ke6 4.Kc6 Rc1+ 5.Kb6 Rd1 drawing.

271) 1.Rb8 (Not 1.d6? Ra7+ 2.Kb6 Ra1.) **1...Ra7+** (1...Ke7? 2.d6+ Ke6 3.Re8+ wins.) **2.Rb7 Ra8 3.Kd7!** (Not yet 3.d6 as 3...Ke6! 4.d7 Ke7 or 4.Rb1 Ra7+ 5.Kb6 Rd7 draws.) **3...Kf6 4.d6 Kf7 5.Rc7!** (5.Kc6+ Ke8 6.Rh7 Ra6+ and Black draws.) **5...Rb8 6.Rc1! Rb7+ 7.Kc6 Rb2 8.Re1!** cutting off the Black King, thus making possible a Lucena's position in a few moves and thereby winning.

272) 1...Ra1! 2.Rc8 (2.Kc7 Ra7+ 3.Kb6 Ra1 draws.) **2...Rd1!** (2...Ra6+ 3.Kd7! Ra7+ 4.Rc7 Ra8 5.d6 wins.) **3.Rc2** (3.Kc6 Ke7 draws.) **3...Ke8 4.Rh2 Rd3 5.Rh8+ Kf7 6.Rd8 Ra3!** and Black's active Rook play will secure the draw.

273) 1.Ra2 Re1 2.Rd2+ Kc7 (Or 2..Kc8, it makes no difference.) **3.Kf8 Rf1 4.f7** and we have Lucena's position, winning for White. Note: With a c- or f-pawn on the 5th or 6th rank, if Black's King is on the "short side" of the pawn he can usually draw-otherwise he loses.

274) 1.Re8! Ra1 2.Kf8 Kg6 3.f7 Kf6 (3...Rf1 4.Re6+ Kh7 5.Ke8 Kg7 6.Re7 wins.) **4.Rb8 Ra6** (Stopping Rb6+.) **5.Kg8** winning.

275) 1.Kf6 Rb8 (1...Rf8+ 2.Kg6 Rg8+ 3.Kf7 wins) **2.Kg6 Rb6+ 3.f6 Rd6 4.Kg7 Rd7+ 5.f7 Rc7 6.Kg8** and **7.f8=Q** wins.

276) 1...Re8+ 2.Kf5 (2.Kd3 Rd8+ 3.Kc2 Rf8 4.Ra4 Kf3 draws–Black's King has broken through the 3rd rank) **2...Rf8+ 3.Kg5 Rg8+ 4.Kh6 Rf8 5.Ra4 Kf3** winning the f-pawn or perpetually checking after **6.Kg5 Rg8+ 7.Kf5 Rf8+,** etc.

277) 1...Rb6!! (Now on 2.Rh8 Black has 2...Rxe6! 3.Rh5+ Kg4 drawing.) **2.e7 Rf6+** (Made possible by 1...Rb6!!.) **3.Kg7 Rg6+ 4.Kh7 Kf6!** (Threatening 5...Rg7+ and 6...Rxe7.) **5.Rf8+ Kxe7** drawing as both Rooks are *en prise.*

278) 1.Kc6! (Not 1.d6? cxd6 2.cxd6 Rg1! and since Black's Rook can check from behind, it's a draw.) **1...Rg6+ 2.d6 Kb8** (Not 2...cxd6?? 3.Rh8#.) **3.Rxc7** winning easily.

279) 1...Rg6! (Not 1...Kb7 2.d6 Rc8 3.c6+ Kb8 4.d7 Rd8 5.Re7 and 6.Re8 winning.) **2.Rh8+ Kd7** (2...Kb7? 3.c6+ Ka7 4.Rh7 Kb8 5.Ka6 Rg8 6.d6! cxd6 7.Kb6 d5 8.Rb7+ Kc8 9.Ra7 Kb8 10.c7+ Kc8 11.Ra8+ wins.) **3.c6+ Kd6** (3...Ke7 4.Rc8 Kd6 5.Rd8+ Ke5 6.Ka6 as in the main line) **4.Rd8+ Ke5 5.Ka6 Rg1** (5...Rd6 6.Rxd6 Kxd6 7.Kb7 wins.) **6.Kb7 Rg7 7.Rd7** winning handily.

280) 1.Kb7 Rb2+ 2.Ka7 Rc2 3.Rh5+ Ka4 (Not 3...Kb4 as after 4.Kb7 the Black Rook can't check from b2.) **4.Kb7 Rb2+ 5.Ka6! Rc2 6.Rh4+ Ka3 7.Kb6** (Threatening 8.Rxh2! Rxh2 9.c8=Q.) **7...Rb2+ 8.Ka5 Rc2 9.Rh3+ Ka2 10.Rxh2!** winning after 10...Rxh2 11.c8=Q.

281) 1.Rd2+ Ke7 2.Rd6!! Kxd6 (2...Rc3 3.Rc6!! Rxc6 4.Ka7 and Queens next.) **3.Kc8 Rc3+ 4.Kd8** and Queens next.

282) 1.Kg5!! Rg1+ 2.Kh6 a1=Q 3.Ra8+! Qxa8 stalemates. Also, if 2...a1=R then 3.Ra8+ Rxa8 is still stalemate; while on 2...a1=N or 2...a1=B then 3.Ra8+ Rg8 4.Rxg8+ Kxg8 is a dead draw.

283) 1.Rg1! Ra8 (1...Rg3+ 2.Kf2 and the g-pawn can't be stopped. Or 1...f3+ 2.Kf2 Ra8 3.g7 Rg8 4.Kxf3 Kh5 5.Kf4 Kh6 6.Kf5! transposes into the main line.) **2.g7 Kh5 3.Kf3 Rg8 4.Kxf4 Kh6 5.Kf5 Kh7** (5...Rxg7 6.Rh1#.) **6.Kf6 Rf8+** (6...Rb8 7.Rh1+ Kg8 8.Rh8#.) **7.gxf8=R!** (Not 7.gxf8=Q stalemate, though 7.gxf8=B (Or N) also wins.) **7...Kh6 8.Rh8#.**

284) 1.Rd8 Kd4 (Now 2.Rxd7? Rxd7+ 3.Kxd7 Kxe5 only draws.) **2.e6! dxe6 3.Kxe6+** winning the Rook. Better than 2...dxe6 is 2...Rf6, though even so 3.Rxd7 wins very quickly.

285) 1.a6 e3 (1...Ra1 2.a7! Kf7 [2...Rxa7? 3.Rh7+ and 4.Rxa7] 3.Rh8! Rxa7 4.Rh7+ wins.) **2.a7 e2 3.a8=Q Rf1+ 4.Kg5 Rg1+** (4...e1=Q 5.Qa7+ Kd8 6.Rh8#.) **5.Kh5 e1=Q 6.Qb7+ Kf8 7.Rf6+ Ke8 8.Qf7+ Kd8 9.Rd6+ Kc8 10.Qd7+ Kb8 11.Rb6+ Ka8 12.Qb7#.**

286) 1.Kb8! (Pushing the Rook to c6 to impose some nice tactics.) **1...Rc6 2.Rf6 c4** (Now 2...Rxf6 3.gxf6 and White Queens first.) **3.Rh6+!** (Forcing the King to the g-file enables the White pawn to Queen with check.) **3...Kg2** (3...Rxh6 4.gxh6 c3 5.h7 winning.) **4.Rxc6! dxc6 5.g6 c3 6.g7 c2 7.g8=Q** with check, winning.

BISHOP VS KNIGHT ENDINGS

In this chapter we see those ancient arch-enemies, the Bishop and Knight, vying for superiority. The Bishop's long range power, enabling it to influence events over the entire board proves the difference in many instances. The Bishop's ability to *temporize* (gain or lose a tempo) is also of great importance, as this trait is not available to the Knight. The bright side for the Knight is its ability to act on squares of either color. This, along with the peculiar ability to jump over other pieces can work in its favor (particularly in blocked positions) when fighting against the Bishop. Both Knight and Bishop have the ability to fork enemy pieces, but the Knight's famous forking powers are far more likely.

We examine many positions where either the Knight or Bishop has one or two extra pawns. In these cases the relative positions of the Kings is normally of decisive importance.

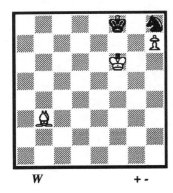

W   + -

No.287
HINT: The poor position of the Knight and the Bishop's ability to win a tempo are decisive. NOTE: A Knight can never gain or lose a tempo.

MODERATE

B   =

No.288
HINT: Black draws by getting rid of White's pawn.

MODERATE

W   + -

No.289
HINT: With the move, White can impose *zugzwang*.

MODERATE

B   =

No.290
HINT: Black to move draws by perpetual check or winning the pawn.

EASY

W   + -

No.291
HINT: With the move White wins by *zugzwang*, which neutralizes the Knight's defensive function.

MODERATE

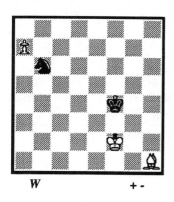

W   + -

No.292
HINT: White maneuvers to eventually win by *zugzwang*.

MODERATE

No.293
HINT: Black to move can draw by a dark-squared blockade.

MODERATE

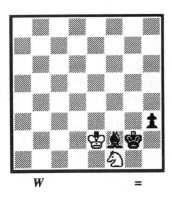

No.294
HINT: White draws by eventually sacrificing the Knight to achieve a drawn Bishop and h-pawn vs King position.

DIFFICULT

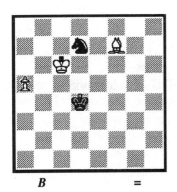

No.295
HINT: Black to move can draw by well-timed threats to win the pawn.

MODERATE

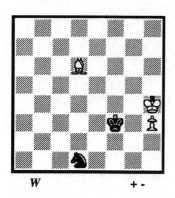

W   + -

No.296

HINT: White allows Black to win his Bishop, since then the pawn can't be stopped.

MODERATE

W   + -

No.297

HINT: The Bishop can dominate the Knight allowing an easy win.

EASY

W   + -

No.298

HINT: Exploitation of the poor position of the cornered Knight.

EASY

W =

No.299

HINT: If the side with the Bishop can immobilize the Knight against the edge of the board, he usually wins. This position is an exception as there are possibilities of stalemate or winning the pawn.

MODERATE

B =

No.300

HINT: With the move, Black can draw by threatening the pawn or achieving perpetual check.

EASY

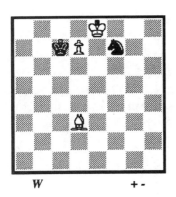

W + -

No.301

HINT: White to move wins by maneuvering for a tempo with the Bishop–a very common motif in Bishop vs Knight endings.

MODERATE

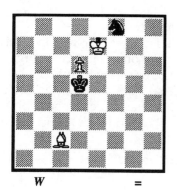

W   =

No.302

HINT: White tries to set up *zugzwang* positions, but by alert defense Black can hold the draw.

DIFFICULT

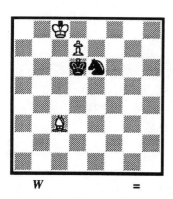

W   =

No.303

HINT: A fundamental drawn position (Also true with the Knight on f7.)

EASY

B   =

No.304

HINT: With the move and excellent King and Knight position, Black can draw.

EASY

W   + -

No.305
HINT: With the move White wins by achieving *zugzwang*. This is identical to example No.304, but with White to move.

MODERATE

W   + -

No.306
HINT: Here, as is so often the case in Bishop vs Knight endings, White wins by achieving *zugzwang*. In this case White triangulates with his King to achieve the goal.

DIFFICULT

W   =

No.307
HINT: White draws with precise tactics, perpetual check being a main theme.

MODERATE

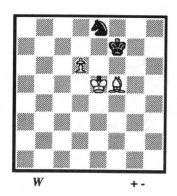

W   + -

No.308
HINT: A sneaky tactic forces the win for White.

MODERATE

W   + -

No.309
HINT: The Knight will be *zugzwanged* away from its defensive role.

MODERATE

B   =

No.310
HINT: Stalemate possibilities allow the draw.

DIFFICULT

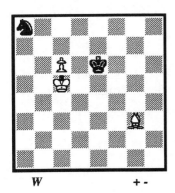

W   + -

No.311
HINT: The poorly placed Knight helps White create a winning *zugzwang* finish.

MODERATE

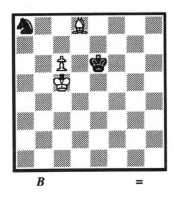

B   =

No.312
HINT: Black draws by pressuring the White pawn.

EASY

W   + -

No.313
HINT: White wins by creating *zugzwang*.

EASY

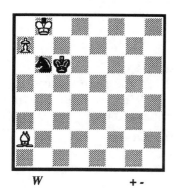

W   + -

No.314
HINT: White wins by restricting the Black Knight.

MODERATE

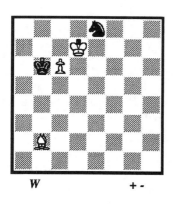

W   + -

No.315
HINT: White must undertake extended maneuvers with his Bishop to enforce a winning *zugzwang*.

DIFFICULT

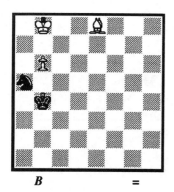

B   =

No.316
HINT: Direct tactics allow Black to draw.

EASY

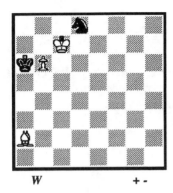

W   + -

No.317
HINT: White maneuvers his Bishop to induce *zugzwang*.

MODERATE

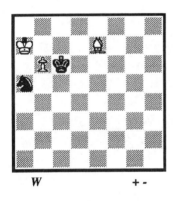

W   + -

No.318
HINT: White induces *zugzwang* to win.

MODERATE

W   + -

No.319
HINT: White's King must move up to help win by *zugzwang*.

MODERATE

W + -

No.320
HINT: Accurate play Queens the pawn or mates soon.

MODERATE

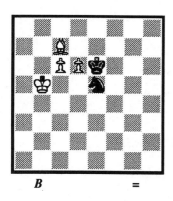

B =

No.321
HINT: Black draws by a Knight sacrifice which allows his King to "eat" the pawn.

DIFFICULT

B =

No.322
HINT: Black can draw by eliminating White's pawns.

EASY

W   + -

No.323
HINT: White can win Black's Knight by *zugzwang*.

EASY

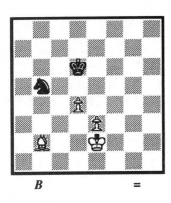

B   =

No.324
HINT: White has erred by just playing d4. Now Black can draw by setting up a light-squared blockade with his King and Knight.

MODERATE

B   =

No.325
HINT: Black draws "instantly" if you choose the right move.

EASY

B =

No.326
HINT: A paradoxical Knight move allows Black to draw by eliminating White's pawns.

MODERATE

B - +

No.327
HINT: Black sacrifices to reach a position in which the Black King dominates play.

DIFFICULT

W =

No.328
HINT: Black seems to be assured of a win until White reveals a subtle stalemate defense.

DIFFICULT

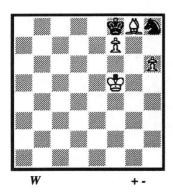

W   + -

No.329
HINT: Careful maneuvering with King and Bishop avoids stalemate defenses.

DIFFICULT

W   + -

No.330
HINT: White wins by cutting off the Bishop's control of a8.

EASY

B   =

No.331
HINT: With the move, Black draws by a clever sacrifice based on "locking in" White's King.

DIFFICULT

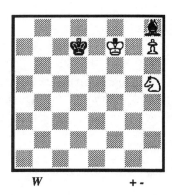

W   + -

No.332

HINT: White wins by avoiding Black's attempts to hem in White's King in front of the h-pawn.

DIFFICULT

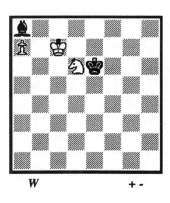

W   + -

No.333

HINT: White maneuvers to block the Bishop's action on the a8-h1 diagonal; then he must avoid Black's attempts to trap his King in front of the pawn.

MODERATE

B   =

No.334

HINT: Black to move draws because he has two diagonals which intersect in front of the pawn, each diagonal being at least 5 squares long. The Black King is not needed to stop the pawn in this case.

MODERATE

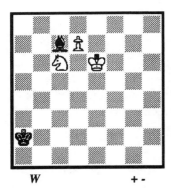

W   + -

No.335

HINT: Because one of the diagonals which intersect in front of White's pawn is less than 5 squares long (And Black's King is poorly placed.), White with the move can win. However, if Black has the move he is able to draw.

MODERATE

B   =

No.336

HINT: With Black to move, his King can come up to help the Bishop and achieve a draw.

MODERATE

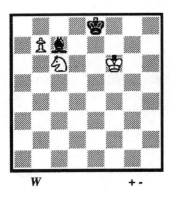

W   + -

No.337

HINT: White's King penetrates Black's position, cooperating with the Knight to force the win.

MODERATE

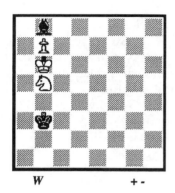

W + -

No.338
HINT: White maneuvers to use his Knight to block the Bishop's diagonal, and Queen the pawn.

EASY

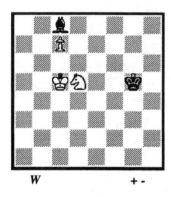

W + -

No.339
HINT: White's King and Knight run off the Bishop and Black's King can't come over to help.

MODERATE

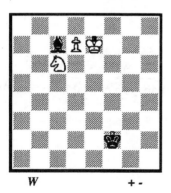

W + -

No.340
HINT: White's King and Knight dominate the Bishop because its King is too far away.

MODERATE

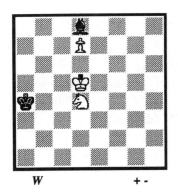

W   + -

No.341
HINT: White wins as Black's King can't assist the Bishop.

MODERATE

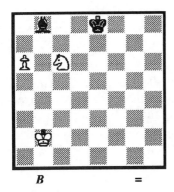

B   =

No.342
HINT: Black finds an ingenious way to transpose into a drawn Knight and pawn ending.

DIFFICULT

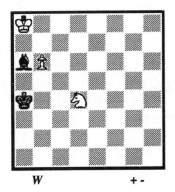

W   + -

No.343
HINT: White's King and Knight outmaneuver the Black King and Bishop. The crucial issue for White is whether to move his King or Knight first–only one choice wins.

MODERATE

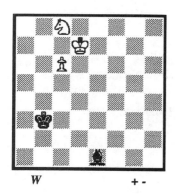

W   + -

No.344
HINT: A tactical trick on White's 2nd move seals the win.

MODERATE

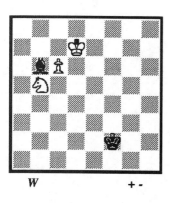

W   + -

No.345
HINT: A simple Knight maneuver drives the Bishop off the a5-d8 diagonal, allowing the pawn to Queen.

EASY

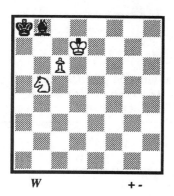

W   + -

No.346
HINT: White's first move uses *zugzwang* to force the issue.

MODERATE

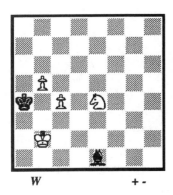

W + -

No.347
HINT: Straightforward play with simple tactics force the win.

EASY

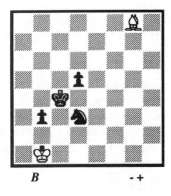

B - +

No.348
HINT: Black shifts his Knight to a more efficient post to assure the Queening of a pawn.

MODERATE

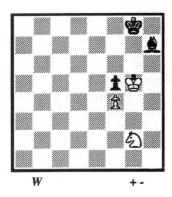

W + -

No.349
HINT: White can't simply attack and win the f-pawn, since Black can obtain the opposition and draw, but White has an amazing pattern of attack leading to mate or winning the Bishop.

DIFFICULT

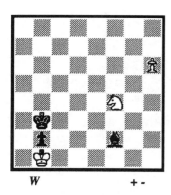

W   + -

No.350
HINT: White's Knight prevents the Bishop from reaching the a1-h8 diagonal.

MODERATE

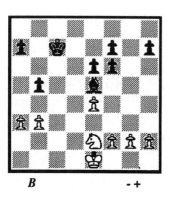

B   - +

No.351
HINT: With pawns on both sides of the board, the Bishop usually outperforms the Knight. The "solution" is from an actual game and is quite long; you should aim to find the first few moves as played, though it is clear there are other paths to victory toward the end. We give the full set of moves for their instructive value.

DIFFICULT

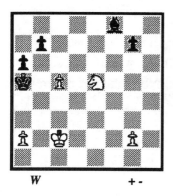

W   + -

No.352
HINT: White wins by rare and beautiful tactical concepts–mating possibilities are hidden in the position.

DIFFICULT

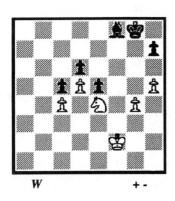

W   + -

No.353

HINT: Black has a "bad" Bishop (i.e., a Bishop whose mobility is hampered by having a significant number of its own pawns on the same color squares as the Bishop.). This often leaves squares of the opposite color (In this case the light-colored squares.) vulnerable to enemy invasion. The "solution" is from an actual game. You should be able to find most of the moves as given, though there are certainly alternative ways to win.

MODERATE

SOLUTIONS FOR EXAMPLES 287-353

287) 1.Bc4! (A waiting move while preparing to shift to the h5-e8 diagonal.) **1...Nf7** (1...Ke8 2.Kg7 wins.) **2.Be2** (Not 2.Bxf7 stalemate. Also, 2.Kg6 Ne5+ 3.Kh6 Ng4+ 4.Kg6 Ne5+ gets nowhere.) **2...Nh8 3.Bh5 Nf7 4.Kg6 Nh8+ 5.Kh6 Ke7 6.Kg7** wins. NOTE: Pawns closer to the edge of the board (Especially an a- or h-pawn.) usually make things difficult for a defending Knight.

288) 1...Nc6! 2.Kxc6 (2.a6 is met by 2...Nb8 [or 2...Nb4] and 3...Nxa6 drawing.) **2...Ka6** and 3...Kxa5 removes the pawn with a dead draw.

289) 1.Bf8! Kh8 (1...Nf6 2.Kxf6 wins as the Bf8 prevents ...Kh6 which could win the pawn.) **2.Kg6 Nf6** (Desperation.) **3.Kxf6** and White wins since his Bishop controls the h8 Queening square–otherwise it would be a well known theoretical draw.

290) 1...Nd7+ 2.Kc8 (Not 2.Ka8??Kc7! and Nb6# cannot be prevented.) **2...Nb6+ 3.Kd8** (3.Kb8 Nd7+ repeats the position.) **3...Kb7** wins the pawn, drawing.

291) 1.Be6! (Stopping ...Nd7 [which would draw if Black had the initial move] and temporizing in order to create a *zugzwang*.) **1...Kc5** (1...Kb5 2.Kb7 Ka5 3.Bd7! Nxd7 4.a8=Q+.) **2.Kb7 Kb5 3.Bd7+! Kc5 4.Bc6** and Black, in *zugzwang*, must lose the Knight or allow the pawn to Queen.

292) 1.Ke2 (Moving up to harass the Knight.) **1...Kf5 2.Ke3 Ke5 3.Kd3 Ke6 4.Kd4 Kd6 5.Bg2!** (Temporizing. Remember that the Bishop has this important ability; the Knight can never gain or lose a tempo by maneuvering.) **5...Kd7 6.Kc5 Kc7 7.Bh1 Nd7+ 8.Kb5 Nb6 9.Bg2!** the final tempo maneuver; the Knight is lost or the pawn Queens next move.

293) 1...Nc8+ 2.Kc6 (Not 2.Kb5 Nd6+, while 2.Ka5 Ka7! securely blockades the pawn on a square of opposite color to the Bishop.) **2...Ka7!** and Black draws as his King sits on the dark square in front of the pawn while the Knight will shuttle back and forth indefinitely.

294) 1.Nh2! Bc5 (1...Kxh7 2.Kxf2 draws as the Black King is trapped in front of the pawn.) **2.Nf3!** (Not 2.Nf1? Bd4! 3.Ke1 Bc3+ 4.Ke2 Bd2! 5.Nxd2 h2.) **2...Bb4 3.Nh4+ Kg3 4.Nf3 Bc3 5.Kf1! Kxf3 6.Kg1** getting to h1 with a simple theoretical draw as the Bishop is the "wrong color" to oust the King.

295) 1...Nb8+ 2.Kb5 (2.Kb7 Kc5! 3.Be8 [3.Kxb8 Kb5 and 4...Kxa5 draws] 3...Kb4 4.Kb6 Kc4 5.Bf7+ Kb4 6.Be6 Ka4 and with the Black King "hovering" next to the a-pawn, White can't win.) **2...Kc3 3.Be6 Kb2 4.Kb6 Ka3 5.Kb7 Kb4** arriving in the nick of time to threaten the pawn and thereby drawing.

296) 1.Kg5 Nf2 2.h4! Ne4+ (2...Ng4 3.h5.) **3.Kg6 Nxd6 4.h5 Nc4 5.h6 Ne5+ 6.Kg7 Kf4 7.h7** and Queens.

297) 1.Bd5! (Hemming in the Knight against the edge of the board, a fairly common possibility in Bishop vs Knight endings.) **1...Ke7 2.Kf5 Kd7 3.Kf6 Ke8 4.e6 Kf8 5.e7+ Ke8 6.Ke6 Nc6 7.Bxc6#.**

298) 1.Kf6! Kc8 2.Kg7 wins the Knight and the game. NOTE: If the Knight is not immobilized and the Black King is on a square of opposite color of the Bishop and in front of the pawn, then it's a draw.

299) 1.Kf5 (1.d7+ Kd8 2.Kd6 Nc4+! 3.Ke6 [3.Bxc4 is stalemate; or if 3.Kc6 Ne5+ and 4...Nxd7] 3...Nb6 and 4...Nxd7 draws.) **1...Kd8 2.Ke4 Kd7 3.Ke5 Kd8!** (Not 3...Ke8? 4.Ke6 Kd8 5.d7 Kc7 6.Ke7 winning.) **4.Kd4 Ke8 5.Kc5 Kd7** tying down the White King to the defense of the pawn and thus drawing.

300) 1...Ne6+ 2.Kd7 Nf8+! 3.Kd8 (3.Kd6 Ng6 wins the pawn.) **3...Ne6+** drawing by perpetual check.

301) 1.Ke7! Nd8 (1...Kc6 2.Bg6! wins.) **2.Be4 Nf7 3.Bf3!** (Temporizing.) **3...Nd8 4.Bd5** winning as the Knight is immobilized, e.g., 4...Nc6+ 5.Bxc6 Kxc6 6.d8=Q.

302) 1.Bd3 Kc6! (1...Kc5 2.Be4! – a *zugzwang* position Black must repeatedly avoid; also, 1...Ke5 2.Be4! Ne6 [forced] 3.d7– another *zugzwang* to avoid.) **2.Bb5+ Kc5** (Of course not 2...Kxb5 3.Kxf8 Kc6 4.Ke7 and 5.d7 wins.) **3.Be8 Kd5 4.Bf7+ Kc6!** (Not 4...Kc5 as 5.Bh5! leads to *zugzwang* positions: 5...Kc6 6.Bf3+ Kc5 7.Be4! *zugzwang,* or 5...Kd5 6.Bf3+ Kc5 [6...Ke5 7.Be4! Ne6 8.d7 wins due to *zugzwang*] 7.Be4! again is *zugzwang*.) **5.Bh5 Kc5! 6.Bf3 Ng6+** (Since 6.Bf3 is not with check, the Knight can now operate successfully.) **7.Ke6 Nf8+ 8.Ke5 Ng6+** drawing easily.

303) 1.Bb4+ Kc6 2.Be7 Kb6 3.Bd8+ Kc6 with a draw.

304) 1...Ne7+ (1...Na7+ also will draw.) **2.Kd8 Nc6+ 3.Ke8 Ke6** with a typical drawing position. NOTE: With White to move in the initial position, he would win. See next position.

305) 1.Bb4+! Ke6 2.Kc7 Kd5 3.Bf8 and it's *zugzwang,* White wins.

306) 1.Kf8! Nh7+ (1...Kh6 2.Kf7 Kg5 3.Bh3 and *zugzwang* wins: 3...Ne4 4.d7 Nd6+ 5.Ke7 Nb7 6.Bg2.) **2.Ke8!** (By triangulating with his King, White will obtain the starting position with Black to move.) **2...Nf6+ 3.Ke7 Kg7** (3...Kg5 4.Kf7 wins.) **4.Bf7!** (It's *zugzwang*.) **4...Ng4 5.Bd5** (Not 5.d7? Ne5! 6.d8=Q Nc6+.) **5...Ne5** (5...Nf6 6.Be4! Ng8+ 7.Ke6 Nf6 8.Bf5 wins.) **6.Be4 Kg8 7.Ke6 Nf7 8.d7 Kf8 9.Kf6 Nd8 10.Bd5** wins.

307) 1.Nf4! f1=Q (1...Be6 2.Ne2+ Kf1 3.Nf4 Bf5 4.Kf3! draws. Also if 1...f1=R then simply 2.Nxd5 is a theoretical draw.) **2.Nh3+ Kh1 3.Nf2+ Kg1 4.Nh3+** drawing by perpetual check.

308) 1.Bg6+! Kxg6 (1...Kf8 2.d7 wins.) **2.d7** and the pawn Queens.

309) 1.Be6+ (Not 1.Bh3 Ne8! 2.d7 Ke7! drawing, as 3...Nf6 and 4...Nxd7 can't be stopped.) **1...Kg6 2.Bc8 Kg7** (2...Kf7 3.Bf5 Kg7 [3...Ne8 4.Bg6+!] 4.Ke6 wins. **3.Bh3 Kg6** (3...Kf7 4.Bf5.) **4.Ke6 Kg7** (4...Ne4 5.Bf5+.) **5.Bf5** winning.

310) 1...Ka8! (Since 2.Kxc8 is stalemate.) **2.Kc6 Nb6!** drawing for if either Bishop or King captures on b6 it is stalemate.

311) 1.Kb5 Kd5 2.Bf4 Ke6 3.Ka6 Kd5 4.Kb7 Kc5 5.Bc1 (Maneuvering to place Black in *zugzwang*.) **5...Kb5** (5...Kd5 6.Ba3 is *zugzwang*.) **6.Be3** wins by *zugzwang*.

312) 1...Ke5 2.Kb5 Kd5 preventing Ka6-b7, the only way for White to attempt to win, and thus drawing.

313) 1.Bd7! winning on the spot as the Black King must not move and Knight moves either lose the Knight or allow the pawn to Queen after BxN.

314) 1.Be6! Kc5 2.Kb7 Kb5 3.Bf7 Kc5 4.Be8! and wins.

315) 1.Be5 Kc5! (1...Kb5 2.Bd4 – *zugzwang*.) **2.Bc3 Kb6 3.Ba5+ Kb5** (3...Kxa5 4.Kxe8.) **4.Bd8 Kc5 5.Bh4 Kb5 6.Bg5!** (Temporizing.) **6...Kc5 7.Be3+ Kd5 8.Bd4! Nd6 9.c7 Kxd4 10.Kxd6** winning.

316) 1...Nc4 2.b7 Nd6 and 3...Nxb7 draws.

317) 1.Bf7! (Heading for e8. Ineffective is 1.Bb3 Kb5 [1...Ka5 2.Bc4! *zugzwang*] 2.Bc4+ Ka5! [not 2...Kxc4? 3.Kxd8 and 4.b7] and White is not making progress.) **1...Kb5** (Not 1...Ka5? 2.Bc4!) **2.Be8+ Ka5** (2...Kc5 3.Bd7! wins) **3.Bd7! Ka6 4.Bf5 Ka5** (4...Kb5 5.Bd3+ Kc5 [5...Ka5 6.Bc4] 6.Bc4! wins) **5.Bg4! Kb5 6.Be2+ Kc5** (6...Ka5 7.Bc4!) **7.Bc4!** wins.

318) 1.Bb4 Nb7 2.Ba3! (Temporizing.) **2...Na5** (2...Nd8 3.Be7 Nb7 4.Ka6 wins.) **3.Ka6 Nb7 4.Be7** and it's *zugzwang*, winning for White.

319) 1.Kd5! Nb4+ (1...Kxf6 loses to 2.Be5+! Kf7 [2...Nxe5 3.g8=Q] 3.Kxc6.) **2.Kd6 Kg8** (2...Nd3 3.g8=Q+! Kxg8 4.Ke7 and 5.f7.) **3.Ba5 Nd3 4.Ke7 Ne5 5.Bc7 Nf7 6.Bf4 Kh7 7.Kf8** (Not 7.Kxf7?? stalemate.) and wins.

320) 1.Bc6! (Not 1.Kxf6?? stalemate.) **1...Nxh7+** (1...Kg7 2.h8=Q+! Kxh8 3.Kxf6 Kg8 4.Bd5+ and 5.g7+ wins.) **2.Kh6! Nf6 3.g7+ Kg8 4.Kg6** and mate next.

321) 1...Kd5 2.d7 Nxc6 3.Kb6 (It looks bad for Black, but....) **3...Nd8! 4.Bxd8 Kd6** wins the pawn, drawing.

322) 1...Nf7 2.g6 (If 2.Kf4 Nxg5! draws since White's Bishop is the "wrong color" to help the h-pawn Queen.) **2...Ne5** and 3...Nxg6 drawing.

323) 1.Bg4 Nf5 2.Kf8 (Not 2.Bxf5?? stalemate.) **2...Ng7 3.Ke7** winning the Knight and the game.

324) 1...Kd5! (Seizing control of the light squares.) **2.Kd3 Nd6** (Stopping e4.) **3.Ba3 Ne4** and it's a draw since White can never advance his pawns while Black's Knight shuttles back and forth, staying in contact with e4.

325) 1...Nxg4+! 2.Bxg4 and it's a theoretical draw since the White Bishop is the "wrong color" to help the h-pawn Queen.

326) 1...Ng8! (Repositioning the Knight to attack the pawns.) **2.Kc4 Ne7 3.f6** (3.Be4 Nxf5! 4.Bxf5 Kxc6 draws.) **3...Nxc6 4.Bxc6 Ke6!** winning the last pawn, drawing.

327) 1...Kb5!! (If the Bishop moves then 2.Nb8 a5 3.Nc6 and 4.Nxa5! draws, since the Bishop is the "wrong color" to help the remaining h-pawn to Queen.) **2.Nxa7+ Kc5!** (Keeping the Knight at bay.) **3.Nc8 a5 4.Ne7 a4 5.Nf5 a3 6.Ne3 a2 7.Nc2 Kc4 8.Kh2 Kc3 9.Na1 Kb2** and wins.

328) 1.Nf6 e3 2.Nd5 Bb6 (2...e2 3.Nf4+ and 4.Nxe2 draws.) **3.Nxe3! Bxe3** it's stalemate!

329) 1.Kf6 Nxf7 2.h7! (Not 2.Bxf7? stalemate.) **2...Nh8 3.Be6 Nf7 4.Kg6 Nh8+ 5.Kh6 Ke7 6.Bg4!** (Not 6.Kg7? Kxe6! 7.Kxh8 Kf7 drawing since the White King can't get out.) **6...Kf7 7.Bf3 Kf6 8.Bh5 Ke7 9.Kg7 Ke6 10.Kxh8 Ke7 11.Kg8** winning.

330) 1.Nb7+ winning on the spot as the pawn Queens.

331) 1...Ba8! 2.Nb7+ (2.Kxa8 Kc7! is a theoretical draw because White's King is trapped in front of his pawn. The Knight can't temporize [as can a Bishop], so it can't chase the Black King away; e.g., 3.Na6+ Kc8 4.Knight moves Kc7. In light of this it should be observed that 2...Kc8?? [with the same intentions as 2...Kc7!] would fail after 3.Na6!, as White's King would get out.) **2...Kd7 3.Kxa8 Kc8!** (Not 3...Kc7?? 4.Nd6! and White's King gets out.) **4.Nd6+ Kc7 5.Nb5+ Kc8** drawing as White's King can't get out.

332) 1.Kf8! (Not 1.Kg8 allowing 1...Ke8! drawing.) **1...Kd8** (1...Ke6 2.Kg8 Ke7 3.Ng7 [not 3.Kxh8 Kf7! draws–3...Kf8? loses] 3...Kf6 4.Kxh8 Kf7 5.Ne6! wins.) **2.Nf4! Kd7** (2...Bc3? 3.Ne6+ Kd7 4.Ng7 and 5.h8=Q.) **3.Kg8 Ke8** (3...Bc3 4.Nh5 and 5.Ng7 wins.) **4.Nh5 Ke7 5.Ng7 Kf6 6.Kxh8 Kf7 7.Ne6!** and White's King escapes, with a quick win.

333) 1.Nc4 Bg2 (1...Ke7 2.Kb8! Kd8 3.Na5 Kd7 4.Nb7 Kc6 5.Kxa8 Kc7 6.Nd6! wins.) **2.Na5 Ba8 3.Kb8 Kd6** (3...Kd7 4.Nb7! wins as in the last note.) **4.Nc4+** (Not 4.Nb7+ Kd7 5.Kxa8 Kc8! drawing.) **4...Kc6 5.Kxa8 Kc7 6.Nd6!** or 6.Nb6! winning.

334) 1...Be8 (White threatened 2.Nc6 and 3.d7.) **2.Nd7 Kg1 3.Kd8 Bg6 4.Ke7 Bf5 5.Nc5 Bc8** (6.Ne6 was threatened.) and it is a draw. Notice how Black's Bishop shifted from one diagonal (a4-e8) to the other (h3-c8) as required, each having five or more squares. Also note that central pawns give rise to longer diagonals than "rim" pawns.

335) 1.Kd5! (Heading for b7 to oust the Bishop.) **1...Ka3** (Or 1...Kb3 2.Nd4+ Kb4 3.Ne6 Ba5 4.Kc6 and 5.Nc7 followed by 6.d8=Q.) **2.Kc4!** (Not 2.Kc5 Ka4! or 2.Nd4 Bd8! 3.Ne6 Bh4 drawing.) **2...Ka4 3.Kc5** (Now Black is in *zugzwang*.) **3...Ka3 4.Kb5 Kb2** (4...Kb3 5.Nd4+ and 6.Ne6.) **5.Ka6 Kc3 6.Kb7** winning.

336) 1...Kb3 2.Kd5 Kc3! (Not 2...Ka4 3.Kc5! winning.) **3.Kc5 Kd3 4.Kb5 Ke4 5.Ka6 Kd5 6.Kb7 Kd6** arriving just in time to draw.

337) 1.Ke6 Kf8 (1...Bg3 2.Ne5 and 3.b8=Q.) **2.Kd7 Bg3 3.Kc8 Ke8 4.Nd4 Bh2 5.Nb5 Ke7 6.Nc7** and 7.b8=Q.

338) 1.Nc7 Kc4 2.Na6 Bg3 3.Nc7 Bf2+ 4.Ka6 and 5.b8=Q.

339) 1.Kc6 Bh3 (1...Kh6 2.Nb6 Ba6 3.Kd7 Kg7 4.Kd8 Kf7 5.Na4 followed by 6.Nc5 wins.) **2.Nb6 Bg2+ 3.Kd7 Bb7 4.Na4 Ba6 5.Kd8 Kf6 6.Nc5** winning.

340) 1.Nd4 (Threat: 2.Ne6 Ba5 3.Kd6 Bb4+ 4.Nc5 Ba5 5.Nb7 Bb6 [5...Bb4+ 6.Ke6] 6.Kc6 winning.) **1...Ke3** (Or 1...Bg3 2.Ne6 Bh4+ 3.Ke8 Ke3 4.Nf8 Ke4 5.Ng6 and 6.Ne7 wins; or 1...Bf4 2.Ne6 Bg3 3.Kf6 Bh4+ 4.Ng5 wins.) **2.Ne6 Ba5 3.Kd6 Bb4+ 4.Nc5 Ba5 5.Nb7 Bb6 6.Kc6** winning.

341) 1.Nc6 Bb6 (1...Bh4 2.Ke6 and 3.Ne7 wins.) **2.Kc4! Bc7** (2...Ka3 3.Kb5 Bc7 4.Ka6 Ka4 5.Kb7 winning.) **3.Kc5!** (*Zugzwang!*) **3...Ka3 4.Kb5 Kb3 5.Ka6 Kc4 6.Kb7** winning.

342) 1...Ba7!! (Not 1...Kd7 2.Nxb8+ Kc7 3.Nd7! wins–White simply brings up his King.) **2.Nxa7 Kd7 3.Nb5 Kc6 4.Kc3 Kb6 5.a7 Kb7 6.Kc4 Ka8 7.Kd5 Kb7 8.Kc5 Ka8** and it's a theoretical draw as White's King can't approach (9.Kb6 stalemates.) and the Knight is tied down to protecting the pawn.

343) 1.Nc6! (Not 1.Ka7 Ka5! 2.Nc6+ Kb5 3.Ne7 Ka5 4.Nf5 Kb5 5.Nd6+ Ka5 6.Ne8 Bc8 [6...Kb5? 7.Nc7+] 7.Nc7 Kb4 8.Kb8 Kc5 9.Nd5 Be6 wins the pawn, drawing.) **1...Bc8** (1...Bb5 2.Kb7! Ka3 3.Kc7 Ba6 4.Nb8 Bf1 5.b7 Bg2 6.Nc6 wins.) **2.Ka7 Kb5 3.Ne7 Ba6 4.Nf5 Ka5 5.Nd6** winning.

344) 1.c7! Ba5 (1...Bf2 2.Nd6.) **2.Nb6! Bxb6 3.c8=Q** wins.

345) 1.Na3 Kf3 2.Nc4 and the Bishop is either captured or the pawn Queens.

346) 1.Ke7! Bg3 (1...Ba7 2.c7 or 2.Nxa7 win.) **2.Nd6 Kb8 3.Kd7 Bxd6 4.Kxd6 Kc8 5.c7 Kb7 6.Kd7** winning.

347) 1.b6! Ba5 2.Nc5+ Kb4 3.b7 Bc7 4.Na6+ Ka5 5.Nxc7 and 6.b8=Q wins.

348) 1...Nc5! (The idea is to play N-a4-b6-c4 to assist the b-pawn.) **2.Bf7 Na4 3.Be8 Nb6 4.Kb2 Kb4 5.Bf7 Nc4+ 6.Kc1 Kc3 7.Bxd5 b2+ 8.Kb1 Nd2+** and the pawn Queens.

349) 1.Kh6! (Tying down the Black King to the defense of the Bishop. The attack on the f-pawn does not win: 1.Nh4 Kg7 2.Nxf5+ Bxf5 3.Kxf5 Kf7 holds the opposition, drawing.) **1...Kh8 2.Nh4 Kg8 3.Nf3! Kh8 4.Ne5 Kg8 5.Nc6! Kh8 6.Ne7 Bg8 7.Ng6#.**

350) 1.Ne6! (Not 1.Ne2 Bh4 and ...Bf6 draws.) **1...Bg3** (1...Bh4 2.Nc5+ Kc4 [2...Kb4 3.Ne4 and 4.h7, 5.h8=Q can't be stopped] 3.Ne4 Kd4 4.h7 wins.) **2.Nd4+ Kc4 3.Nf3** winning easily.

351) 1...Bb2! (The first step is to force a weakening pawn move to allow the King to penetrate later.) **2.a4 bxa4 3.bxa4 Kc6!** (Not 3...Kb6 4.Kd2 Ka5 5.Kc2 Be5 6.f4 Bd6 7.Kb3 and White can hold.) **4.Kd2 Kc5 5.Nc3** (5.Kc2 Bd4! 6.f3 [6.Nxd4 Kxd4 7.f3 Kc4 8.Kb2 Kb4 wins] 6...Kc4 7.Nc1 Be5 8.h3 Kb4 wins.) **5...Kb4 6.Nb5 a5 7.Nd6 Kxa4 8.Kc2** (8.Nxf7 Kb3 9.Nd8 a4 10.Nxe6 a3 11.Nc5+ Kc4 12.Nd3 a2 winning.) **8...Be5** (The Bishop's long range and ability to strike at both sides of the board simultaneously are clearly evident here.) **9.Nxf7 Bxh2 10.Nd8 e5 11.Nc6 Bg1 12.f3 Bc5 13.Nb8 Kb5 14.g4 Be7 15.g5** (Desperation.) **15...fxg5 16.Nd7 Bd6 17.Nf6 Kc4** all from a famous game Chekhover-Lasker, Moscow 1935. White resigned since 18.Nxh7 Be7! traps the Knight and otherwise Black is simply two pawns up.

352) 1.c6!! bxc6 (1...Kb6 2.Nd7+ and 3.Nxf8, or 1...Bd6 2.Nc4+ and 3.Nxd6.) **2.Kb3!** (Threatening 3.a4 and 4.Nc4#!) **2...Kb5** (Or 2...Kb6 3.Nd7+ and 4.Nxf8; on 2...Be7 3.Nxc6+; if 2...Bc5 then 3.Nc4+ Kb5 4.a4#; finally, 2...c5 3.a4 Kb6 [forced] 4.Nd7+.) **3.a4+ Kb6** (3...Ka5 4.Nc4#.) **4.Nd7+** and 5.Nxf8 winning.

353) 1.g5 (Clearing the way for the King to penetrate on the weakened light squares.) **1...Kg7 2.Kf3 Kf7 3.Kg4 Be7 4.Kf5 Bf8 5.Nf6 h6 6.gxh6 Bxh6 7.Ne4 Bf8 8.h6!** Bxh6 (8...Be7 9.h7 Kg7 10.Ke6 Bf8 11.h8=Q+ Kxh8 12.Kf7 Bh6 13.Nxd6 Bg5 14.Ne4 Be3 15.d6 winning quickly.) **9.Nxd6+ Ke7 10.Ne4 Be3 11.d6+ Kd7 12.Kxe5 Kc6** (Otherwise 13.Kd5 and 14.Nxc5.) **13.Ke6 Bg1 14.d7 Kc7 15.Ke7** winning easily.

ROOK AND MINOR PIECE ENDINGS

In this chapter we see the "heavy-weight" Rook battling it out against Knight, Bishop, Bishop and Knight, two Bishops, and two Knights. These positions are illustrated with and without pawns.

You might be surprised to know that the Rook often cannot defeat a lone Knight or Bishop, but you must absorb the drawing techniques in these examples to achieve the save. Even more surprising, a lone Knight or Bishop can sometimes fend off a Rook and pawn–find out how!

On the other hand, a well-placed Rook may display its mettle in staving off minor piece(s) and pawn(s)–sometimes even advanced connected passers with a minor piece can be handled.

King placement, as in most endings, plays a decisive part in many of these examples. His majesty often is seen in the role of avenging hero, coordinating with his minions to gain the victory, or hapless victim of relentless mating threats and finessful tactical blows.

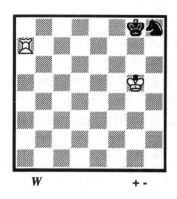

W   + -

No.354
HINT: White takes advantage of the Knight's poor position in the corner.

EASY

W   + -

No.355
HINT: White can win the Knight.

EASY

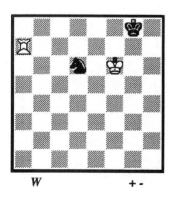

W   + -

No.356
HINT: White makes progress by temporizing waiting moves (Most of them by the Rook.) to cut down the flight squares of the Knight. Eventually, White wins the Knight because of a mating threat.

DIFFICULT

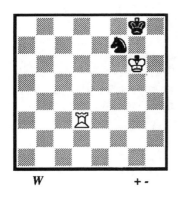

W   + -

No.357
HINT: White corrals the Knight soon winning it.

MODERATE

B   =

No.358
HINT: Black can draw by checking the White King as it tries to invade.

EASY

B   =

No.359
HINT: With the move, Black draws. There is only one correct first move.

MODERATE

B =

No.360
HINT: With the move, Black can draw by checking away the White King as it approaches.

EASY

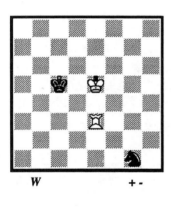

W +-

No.361
HINT: White can trap the Knight. A subtle temporizing move begins the process.

MODERATE

W +-

No.362
HINT: When the defending King and Knight are widely separated, the win is usually there. The Knight is eventually driven to the edge of the board, where it is "surrounded" by White's forces.

MODERATE

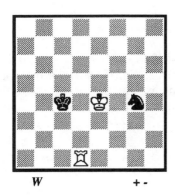

W   + -

No.363

HINT: White steadily narrows down the Knight's moves.

MODERATE

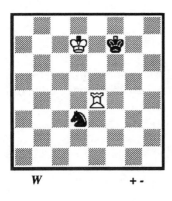

W   + -

No.364

HINT: Black's King and Knight are widely separated, so White can force the win of the Knight. The Rook will reduce the Knight's mobility and eventually the Knight will be trapped against the side of the board.

DIFFICULT

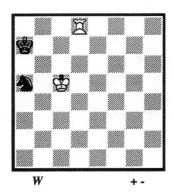

W   + -

No.365

HINT: With the move, White combines threats to pin and win the Knight, hem in and win it, along with mating threats to force victory.

EASY

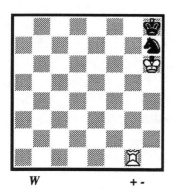

W   + -

No.366
HINT: With the move, White wins using mating threats, threats to the Knight and *zugzwang*.

MODERATE

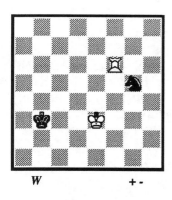

W   + -

No.367
HINT: White to move can quickly drive the Knight to the edge of the board, winning it.

EASY

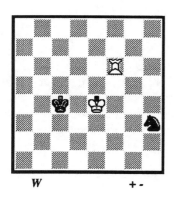

W   + -

No.368
HINT: White traps the Knight in four moves.

MODERATE

B   =

No.369
HINT: White could win by marching his King to b7; the key to Black's defense is to get his own King to c8 to prevent this.

DIFFICULT

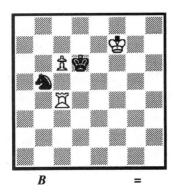

B   =

No.370
HINT: Black must find a forcing first move to earn the draw.

MODERATE

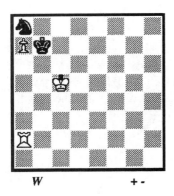

W   + -

No.371
HINT: White finds a surprising first move which sets up the win of the Knight.

MODERATE

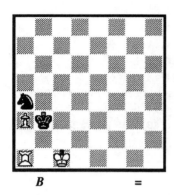

B =

No.372
HINT: Black can draw by blockading the pawn, even winning it if White tries to mobilize his King.

EASY

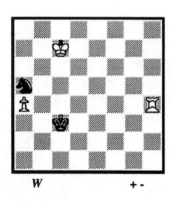

W + -

No.373
HINT: White can enforce the pawn's advance by sacrificing.

EASY

B =

No.374
HINT: Black draws by maneuvering to win the pawn.

EASY

No.375
HINT: Black draws by a cute stalemate defense.

MODERATE

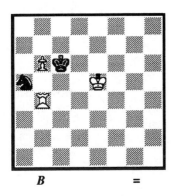

No.376
HINT: Forcing tactics allow Black to draw.

EASY

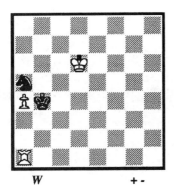

No.377
HINT: White sacrifices his Rook to race the pawn in to a8.

MODERATE

B   =

No.378
HINT: Black draws because his King is ideally placed in front of the pawns, and his Rook is well-posted to harass White's forces from behind.

MODERATE

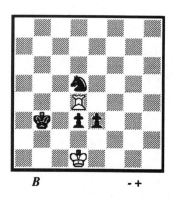

B   - +

No.379
HINT: With the move, Black's well-coordinated King and Knight win quickly.

EASY

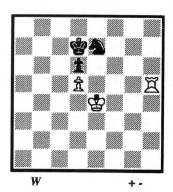

W   + -

No.380
HINT: White wins by a timely sacrifice to obtain a won King and pawn ending.

DIFFICULT

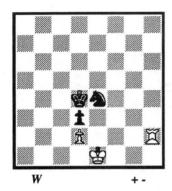

W   + -

No.381
HINT: White needs to activate his Rook while occasionally using *zugzwang* to earn the win.

MODERATE

B   =

No.382
HINT: Black draws by getting rid of White's pawn.

MODERATE

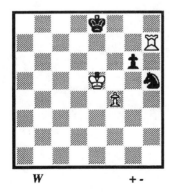

W   + -

No.383
HINT: With the move, White takes advantage of the Knight's dependency on the g-pawn.

EASY

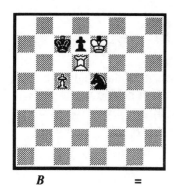

B =

No.384
HINT: Black draws by eliminating White's pawn.

MODERATE

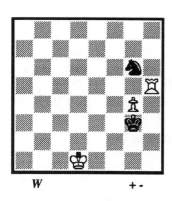

W + -

No.385
HINT: Alert tactical play allows White to take advantage of an unprotected Knight at the end of the winning maneuvers.

MODERATE

W + -

No.386
HINT: A most unexpected sacrifice forces the win.

DIFFICULT

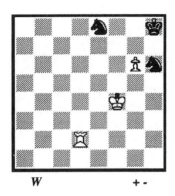

W   + -

No.387
HINT: Nifty tactics can lead to a piquant and rare mating pattern.

MODERATE

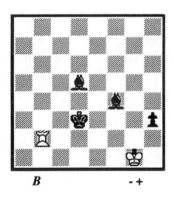

B   - +

No.388
HINT: Black wins by a clever "driving" maneuver, culminating in *zugzwang*.

MODERATE

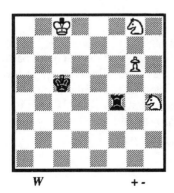

W   + -

No.389
HINT: White wins by elegant Knight pirouettes.

DIFFICULT

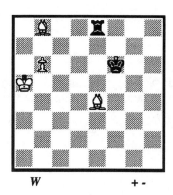

W   + -

No.390
HINT: Deep tactical maneuvers force the win. White starts with a Bishop sacrifice.

DIFFICULT

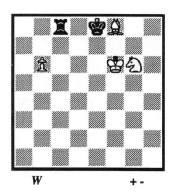

W   + -

No.391
HINT: White's well-coordinated pieces defeat Black's "flat-footed" King and Rook. White begins with a piece sacrifice.

DIFFICULT

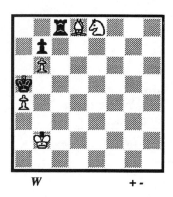

W   + -

No.392
HINT: A furious tactical battle. Near the end, Black seems to have a miraculous drawing resource; but further scrutiny reveals a winning trump for White.

DIFFICULT

W   + -

No.393
HINT: Ingenious tactics involving sacrifice, countersacrifice and an unusual *zugzwang* position lead to White's win.

DIFFICULT

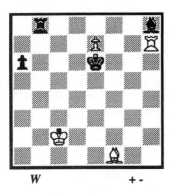

W   + -

No.394
HINT: A brilliant Bishop sacrifice on the 2nd move sets up a following discovered double check which sweeps the Black army from the board.

DIFFICULT

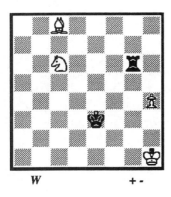

W   + -

No.395
HINT: White's first move is a shattering blow which sets up a bewildering array of Knight forks.

MODERATE

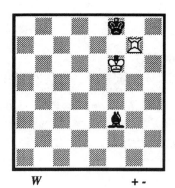

W   + -

No.396
HINT: White switches his Rook from file to rank, pursuing the hapless Bishop to it's doom.

DIFFICULT

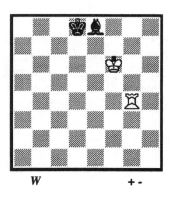

W   + -

No.397
HINT: White's 2nd move creates a *zugzwang* which soon leads to the win of the Bishop.

MODERATE

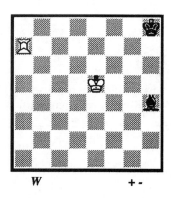

W   + -

No.398
HINT: White combines mating threats with threats to win the Bishop to force victory.

DIFFICULT

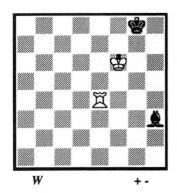

No.399
HINT: White's first move creates a *zugzwang*, soon winning the Bishop.

MODERATE

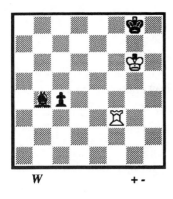

No.400
HINT: White's Rook maneuvers to create threats to the back rank and the Bishop using *zugzwang* when necessary to make progress.

DIFFICULT

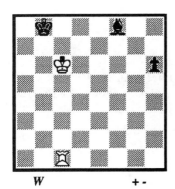

No.401
HINT: White's Rook can win the Bishop by setting up a pin.

MODERATE

B - +

No.402
HINT: After some preliminaries, the Black King strolls to the Queenside to allow the pawn to Queen.

MODERATE

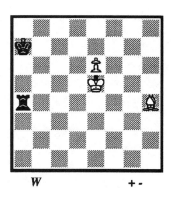

W + -

No.403
HINT: A subtle sacrifice of the Bishop enables the pawn to Queen.

DIFFICULT

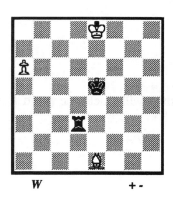

W + -

No.404
HINT: White's Bishop works to control key squares, allowing the pawn to Queen.

MODERATE

W   + -

No.405
HINT: A sneaky sacrifice of the Bishop paves the way for the pawn to Queen.

DIFFICULT

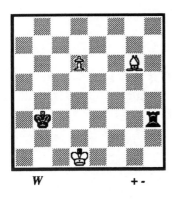

W   + -

No.406
HINT: White's King and Bishop cooperate to perfection to stymie the Rook's efforts to stop the pawn.

MODERATE

W   + -

No.407
HINT: At critical junctures, the Bishop will shield the pawn from the Rook.

MODERATE

W   + -

No.408
HINT: White uses tactical finesses to defeat the Rook's back rank defense.

DIFFICULT

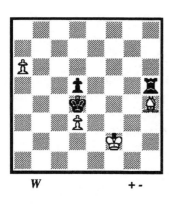

W   + -

No.409
HINT: The Bishop dominates the Rook with various tactical blows.

DIFFICULT

B   - +

No.410
HINT: The decisive motif at the end involves the Bishop shielding off the Rook from the Queening square. Note that if White has the move, he can draw.

MODERATE

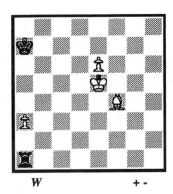

W + -

No.411

HINT: On the 3rd and 5th moves White offers the sacrifice of the Bishop to lure the Rook (Or King.) to an unfavorable square.

DIFFICULT

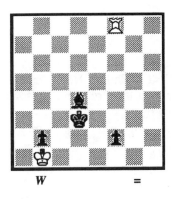

W =

No.412

HINT: This is the same position as example No.410, but with White to move he can draw.

EASY

W =

No.413

HINT: White offers up his Rook on the 2nd move, which draws by stalemate if it's taken. On White's 5th move, an even more fantastic Rook sacrifice assures a draw by stalemate or by winning the pawn the following move.

DIFFICULT

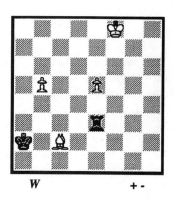

W   + -

No.414
HINT: White's Bishop works to control key squares to shepherd in the pawn.

MODERATE

W   =

No.415
HINT: White's Rook sacrifices itself on the 3rd move to force a draw by stalemate.

DIFFICULT

W   + -

No.416
HINT: White sacrifices two pawns to reach a position in which the Bishop performs shielding duty for the last pawn to Queen.

DIFFICULT

B   **=**

No.417
HINT: Black can sacrifice the Rook to reach a theoretically drawn Bishop and a-pawn ending.

MODERATE

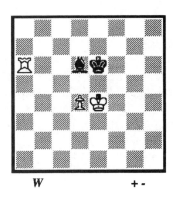

W   **+ -**

No.418
HINT: White uses *zugzwang* to press forward with his pawn.

EASY

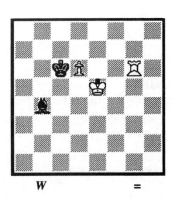

W   **=**

No.419
HINT: Black can draw by threats to capture the pawn.

EASY

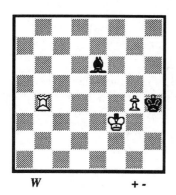

W   + -

No.420
HINT: White sacrifices the pawn to take advantage of the position of Black's King and Bishop.

MODERATE

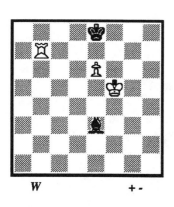

W   + -

No.421
HINT: White will sacrifice his pawn in order to be able to take advantage of the Bishop's exposed position. It is not an easy task, requiring purposeful maneuvering.

DIFFICULT

B   =

No.422
HINT: Black draws by stalemate or transposing into a drawn Bishop vs Rook ending.

MODERATE

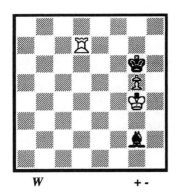

W   + -

No.423
HINT: With the b- or g-pawn, it's usually a win because the defenders have less space to maneuver in near the edge of the board.

EASY

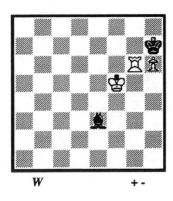

W   + -

No.424
HINT: White sacrifices his pawn to enter a winning Rook vs Bishop ending.

DIFFICULT

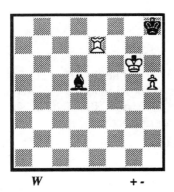

W   + -

No.425
HINT: White wins by creating back rank threats.

EASY

B =

No.426
HINT: With correct Bishop maneuvers, Black can stop White's attempts to win.

MODERATE

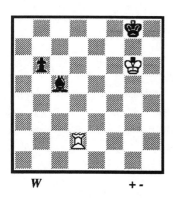

W + -

No.427
HINT: Black's extra pawn doesn't draw due to serious back rank tactics.

EASY

W =

No.428
HINT: White draws by confining the Black King to the 1st rank and preventing the Rook from becoming active.

EASY

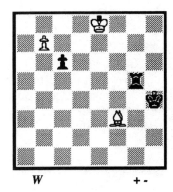

W   + -

No.429
HINT: White's winning procedure begins with a Bishop sacrifice utilizing the problem-like themes of "interference" and "attraction".

DIFFICULT

B   =

No.430
HINT: A stunning sacrifice forces the draw.

MODERATE

W   + -

No.431
HINT: White maneuvers the Bishop to a better diagonal and uses *zugzwang* to force the win.

MODERATE

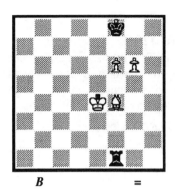

B =

No.432
HINT: Black begins by playing waiting moves with his Rook until a critical moment, then a surprising sacrifice of the Rook on an "empty" square forces the draw.

DIFFICULT

SOLUTIONS FOR EXAMPLES 354-432

354) 1.Kf6 winning the Knight as 1...Kf8 allows 2.Ra8#.

355)1.Kg6 threatening both 2.Ra8# and 2.Kxh6.

356)1.Ra5! (A high-class waiting move.) **1...Nc4** (1...Nc8 2.Ra8 wins the Knight; or 1...Nb7 2.Ra8+ Kh7 3.Ra7; if 1...Ne8+ then 2.Ke7 Ng7 3.Rg5! Kh7 4.Kf7 Kh8 5.Rg1! [not 5.Rxg7?? stalemate] wins; 1...Kh7 2.Rh5+ Kg8 3.Rd5 Nc4 4.Rd4 Ne3 [4...Nb2 5.Ke6 Kg7 6.Kd5 Kf6 7.Kc6! Ke5 8.Kc5 Ke6 9.Kb5 Ke5 10.Rd2 wins] 5.Kg6 Kf8 6.Rf4+ Kg8 7.Re4 wins.) **2.Ra4! Nd6** (2...Nb2 3.Rd4!; or 2...Nd2 3.Rg4+ Kh7 4.Rf4! Kg8 [4...Nb3 5.Rh4+ Kg8 6.Rg4+ Kh7 7.Rg7+ Kh8 8.Kf7 wins] 5.Kg6!.) **3.Rd4 Ne8+** (3...Nb5 4.Rd3! Kh7 5.Kf7! Kh6 6.Ke7! Kg6 [6...Nc7 7.Kd7 Na6 8.Rd6+] 7.Kd7 Kf6 8.Kc6 Na7+ 9.Kb7 Nb5 10.Kb6 wins.) **4.Ke7 Nc7** (4...Ng7 5.Rd5!.) **5.Rg4+ Kh7 6.Kf7 Kh6 7.Rg6+ Kh7** (7...Kh5 8.Rc6 wins.) **8.Rb6! Nd5 9.Rb5 Nf4 10.Rf5** wins.

357) 1.Rd5! (Hemming-in the Knight.) **1...Nh8+** (1...Kf8 2.Rf5.) **2.Kf6 Nf7** (2...Kh7 3.Rg5 Kh6 4.Rg7!.) **3.Rd7 Nh6** (3...Nh8 4.Ra7.) **4.Kg6** winning the Knight.

358) 1...Nh6 (The only move, but quite good enough.) **2.Kf6** (2.Rh7 Ng8 3.Rh8 Kg7 holds.) **2...Ng8+** (Keeping White's King at bay.) **3.Kg6 Ne7+ 4.Kf6 Ng8+** and draws as White is getting nowhere.

359) 1...Ne7! (Others lose: 1...Nd6 2.Kb6! Kb8 3.Kc6+, or 1...Na7 2.Kb6! Kb8 3.Rb2! Nc8+ 4.Kc6+ Ka8 5.Kc7 wins.) **2.Kb6 Kb8! 3.Re1 Nc8+ 4.Kc6 Na7+** and Black draws as White can make no progress.

360) 1...Nf7+ (Not 1...Kf8? 2.Rc8 Ke8 3.Ra8.) **2.Ke6 Nd8+ 3.Kf6 Kf8 4.Rd7 Ke8** (Not 4...Nc6? 5.Rd6 winning due to the mate threat on d8.) **5.Re7+ Kf8 6.Re1 Nb7 7.Ke6 Ke8 8.Rb1 Nd8+ 9.Kd6 Nf7+** and White gets nowhere.

361) 1.Kf5! (Not 1.Kf4? Kd4! drawing, e.g., 2.Re1 Nh3+ 4.Kg3 Ng5 5.Kf4 Nh3+,etc..) **1...Kd4 2.Kf4** (Now the Black King must move away.) **2...Kc4 3.Kg3 Kd4 4.Re1** winning the Knight.

362) 1.Rf3! (Limiting the Knight's mobility.) **1...Kg6** (1...Nb2 2.Kd5 Kg6 3.Kd4 Kg5 [3...Na4 4.Rb3! and 5.Rb4 wins the Knight] 4.Rf1! Kg4 5.Rb1 Na4 6.Rb4 wins.) **2.Ke5 Kg5 3.Kd4 Kg4 4.Rf1 Nb2 5.Rb1 Na4 6.Rb4** wins the Knight.

363) 1.Rf1! Nh6 (1...Nh2 2.Rg1 and 3.Kf4 and Kg3 wins the Knight.) **2.Rf4 Ng8 3.Rf7!** (Limiting the Knight's moves.) **3...Nh6** (3...Kc5 4.Ke5 Kc6 5.Rg7 Nh6 6.Kf6 and 7.Kg5 wins the Knight.) **4.Rg7 Kc5 5.Kf4** and **6.Kg5** wins the Knight.

364) 1.Re3! Nc5+ (Or 1...Nb4 2.Kd6 Nc2 [2...Kf6 3.Rc3! wins] 3.Re4 Na3 4.Kc5 Nb1 5.Kb4 Nd2 6.Re2 wins the Knight; or 1...Nb2 2.Kc6 Nc4 [2...Nd1 3.Rd3 Nb2 4.Rd4 wins, as does 2...Kf6 3.Kd5 Kf5 4.Rb3 Nd1 5.Rd3 Nb2 6.Rd4] 3.Re4 Na5+ [3...Nd2 4.Rf4+ Kg6 5.Kd5 Kg5 6.Rf2 wins] 4.Kd7 Nb3 [4...Nb7 5.Re5 wins] 5.Kd6 Kf6 [5...Nd2 6.Rf4+ Kg6 7.Kd5] 6.Kd5 Kf5 7.Re3 Nd2 8.Rd3 winning.) **2.Kd6 Nb7+ 3.Kc6 Na5+** (3...Nd8+ 4.Kd7 Nb7 5.Re5.) **4.Kd7! Nc4 5.Rf3+ Kg6 6.Ke6 Kg5** (6...Nd2 7.Rf4! Kg5 [7...Nb3 8.Kd5 Nc1 9.Kc4 Ne2 10.Rf2] 8.Ke5 Nb3 9.Rf2 Kg4 10.Rc2! Kg5 11.Rb2 Nc5 12.Rb5! wins.) **7.Rd3! Nb6 8.Rd4! Kg6 9.Rb4 Nc8 10.Kd7 Na7 11.Rb7** winning the Knight.

365) 1.Kb5 Nb7 (1...Nb3 2.Rd1! and 3.Kb4 traps the Knight.) **2.Rd7 Kb8 3.Kb6 Ka8 4.Rh7** (Not 4.Rxb7?? stalemate.) **4...Nd8** (4...Nd6 5.Rh8+.) **5.Rh8** pinning the Knight, winning the Knight, and mating next move.

366) 1.Kg6! Kg8 (1...Nf8+ 2.Kf7 Nh7 [2...Nd7 3.Rh1#] 3.Rg8#.) **2.Rg2!** (*Zugzwang!*.) **2...Nf8+** (2...Kh8 3.Kf7 wins.) **3.Kf6+ Kh8** (3...Kh7 4.Kf7 threatens both 5.Kxf8 and 5.Rh2#.) **4.Kf7** mating quickly.

367) 1.Kf4 Nh3+ (1...Nh7 2.Rf7 wins the Knight.) **2.Kg4 Ng1 3.Rf2 Kc3 4.Rg2** winning the Knight.

368) 1.Rf5! (Stopping Ng5.) **1...Kc3** (1...Ng1 2.Ke3 Nh3 3.Rh5 Ng1 4.Rh1.) **2.Ke3 Kc2** (2...Ng1 3.Kf2 Nh3+ 4.Kg2.) **3.Rh5 Ng1 4.Rh1** wins.

369) 1...Ne7! (The right way. On 1...Nb6? 2.Kd4 Kc8 3.Rc6! Na8 [3...Na4 4.Ra6 wins the Knight] 4.Kd5 Nxc7+ 5.Kd6 wins.) **2.Ke4 Nc8 3.Kd5 Ne7+ 4.Kc4 Kc8! 5.Kb5** (5.Re5 Nc6 draws.) **5...Kb7** heading off White's King and securing the draw.

370) 1...Na7! (Forcing the pawn to advance, the key to Black's defense.) **2.c7 Kd7 3.Kf6 Nc8 4.Ke5 Ne7** reaching a theoretical draw.

371) 1.Rb2+! Kxa7 (1...Kc7 2.Rb8 wins.) **2.Kc6** wins the Knight as 2...Ka6 allows 3.Ra2#.

372) 1...Nc5 (Simply waiting.) **2.Kd2** (What else?.) **2...Kb2!** winning the pawn and drawing easily. Note that the short distance between the Ra1 and the a3 pawn makes this possible.

373)1.Kb6 Nc4+ (1...Nb3 2.a5 wins.) **2.Rxc4+! Kxc4 3.a5** winning.

374) 1...Na3! 2.Ke5 Kb5 3.Kd5 (3.Kd4 Kxb4.) **3...Nc2** winning the pawn and drawing.

375) 1...Kb8! 2.a7+ (2.Rg6 Ka7 threatens 3...Nxa6, drawing easily.) **2...Ka8!,** the point, now 3.Rxc7 stalemates and otherwise Black plays 3...Nb5 winning the pawn.

376) 1...Kc5! drawing immediately, since if the Rook moves laterally then Kxb6 draws, while if the Rook retreats down the b-file then 2...Nc4+ and 3...Nxb6 does the trick.

377) 1.Kc7 Nb3 (Now if 2.Rb1 Kxa4 draws, while 2.Ra2 Nc1 3.Rc2 [3.Ra1 Nb3 repeats the position] 3...Nb3 gets White nowhere.) **2.Kb6!** (A brilliant Rook sacrifice to mobilize the pawn.) **2...Nxa1 3.a5 Nb3 4.a6 Nc5 5.a7 Nd7+ 6.Kc7** and **7.a8=Q** wins.

378) 1...Rd2 (Simply waiting.) **2.Ke5** (Or 2.Kc5 Ke7 3.Nc6+ Kxe6 4.d8=Q Rxd8 5.Nxd8+ drawing.) **2...Kc7! 3.Nb5+ Kc6**

4.Kf6 (Hoping for 4...Kxb5? 5.Ke7! winning.) **4...Rxd7!** and now 5.exd7 Kxd7 draws.

379) 1...Nc3+ 2.Ke1 (2.Kc1 Ne2+ [not 2...d2+? 3.Rxd2!] drawing.) **2...Kc2 3.Rd7 d2+** winning easily.

380) 1.Kf4 Kd8 2.Rh8+ Kd7 3.Rh7 Kd8 4.Rxe7! Kxe7 5.Kg5 Kf7 6.Kf5 Ke7 7.Kg6! (Outflanking the Black King.) **7...Ke8 8.Kf6 Kd7 9.Kf7 Kc8 10.Ke6 Kc7 11.Ke7 Kc8 12.Kxd6 Kd8 13.Ke6 Ke8 14.d6 Kd8 15.d7 Kc7 16.Ke7** wins.

381) 1.Rh4 Kd5 2.Rh8 Kd4 3.Rd8+ Kc4 4.Rd7! (A waiting move.) **4...Nc5 5.Rd6 Ne4 6.Rd8!** (Another waiting move, out of range of the Knight.) **6...Nc5 7.Kf2** (Now, due to *zugzwang* the Knight has to move, allowing White's King decisive entry.) **7...Ne4+ 8.Ke3 Nc5 9.Rd4+ Kb5 10.Rxd3 Nxd3 11.Kxd3** with an easy win in this King and pawn ending.

382) 1...b3! 2.Rb8+ (2.a3 b2! 3.Rb8+ Ka4 4.Rxb2 Kxa3 is a drawn Rook vs Knight ending.) **2...Ka4 3.axb3+ Nxb3+** and the Rook vs Knight ending in a draw.

383) 1.f5! (Since 1...gxf5? loses the Knight.) **1...Kf8 2.fxg6** winning easily.

384) 1...Nc4! 2.Rxd7+ Kc6 and draws as the c-pawn falls, resulting in a theoretically drawn Rook vs Knight ending.

385) 1.Rh6! (Not 1.Rg5 Nf4 2.Rg8 Ne6! 3.Rg6 Nf4 4.Rg8 Ne6 repeating the position, drawing.) **1...Ne5 2.g5 Nf7** (2...Kg4 3.g6 Kg5 4.g7! wins.) **3.Rh5! Ne5** (3...Kg4 4.g6!.) **4.g6!** winning as 4...Nxg6 loses to 5.Rg5+.

386) 1.Rxa8+!! Nxa8 (1...Kxa8 2.Kxc7 Ka7 3.Kc6 Ka8 4.Kxb6 Kb8 transposes into our main line. Also, if 1...Kb7 then 2.Ra7+! Kxa7 3.Kxc7 likewise wins..) **2.Kc8 Nc7 3.Kxc7 Ka8 4.Kxb6 Kb8 5.Kc6 Kc8 6.b6 Kb8 7.b7 Ka7 8.Kc7** wins.

387) 1.Kg5! Ng8 (On 1...Kg7 2.Rd7+ and 3.Kxh6.) **2.Rh2+ Kg7** (The "better" 2...Nh6 3.Kxh6 loses prosaically.) **3.Rh7+ Kf8 4.Rf7#.**

388) 1...Kc3! (The key move. The idea is to drive the Rook off the 2nd rank by *zugzwang*.) **2.Re2 Kb3!** (It's *zugzwang* –the Rook has no safe squares on the 2nd rank, and if it leaves the 2nd then 3...h2 and 4...h1=Q wins.) **3.Kf1 h2** winning.

389) 1.Nf6! (Since 1...Rxf6 fails to 2.g7!.) **1...Rf1** (So that 2.g7 is met by 2...Rg1 and 3.g8=Q Rxg8 4.Nxg8 is a draw–two lone Knights can't force mate.) **2.Nf3! Rxf3** (2...Rf2 3.Ne4+.) **3.g7 Rg3 4.Ne4+ K-moves** and **5.Nxg3,** winning easily.

390) 1.Bc7! Rxe4 2.Bd8+! (To block the back rank.) **2...Kf7 3.b7 Re1 4.Ka6!** (Not 4.b8=Q? Ra1+ 5.Kb6 Rb1+ drawing.) **4...Ra1+ 5.Ba5 Rb1 6.Bb6 Ra1+ 7.Kb5 Rb1+ 8.Kc5 Rc1+ 9.Kd4 Rd1+ 10.Kc3 Rc1+ 11.Kb2** and the pawn Queens.

391) 1.Ne5! Kxf8 (1...Rb8 2.Bc5! wins: 2...Kd8 3.Nc6+, or 2...Rc8 3.Bd6! and 4.b7 wins.) **2.b7 Rd8** (2...Rb8? 3.Nd7+.) **3.Nd7+! Ke8** (3...Kg8 4.Ke7! wins.) **4.Ke6!** (*Zugzwang*.) **4...Rxd7 5.b8=Q+** wins.

392) 1.Nd6! (Since 1...Rxd8 loses to 2.Nxb7+ and 3.Nxd8.) **1...Rc6 2.Nxb7+ Ka6** (2...Kxa4 3.Bc7 Kb5 4.Nd6+ Rxd6 5.b7! Rd8! 6.Bxd8 Ka6 [now 7.b8=Q is stalemate, but...] 7.b8=R! wins.) **3.Na5! Kxa5** (3...Rc8 4.Bc7 wins.) **4.b7+ Rb6+! 5.Bxb6+ Ka6!** (Black fights back resourcefully. Now b8=Q or Rook stalemates.) **6.b8=N+!** (The only way to win. Note that 6.b8=B only draws since both Bishops are the wrong color to promote the a-pawn.) **6...Kxb6 7.Kb3** wins.

393) 1.Ra4! (Threat: 2.Rxb4+ Kxb4 3.Be1.) **1...Ra3!** (A fine retort. Now 2.Rxa3? Bxa3+ 3.Kxa3 Kc3! wins the pawn with a certain draw.) **2.Rxb4+! Kxb4 3.Be1+** (Not 3.Bc5+? Kxc5 4.Kxa3 Kc4 and the ending is drawn since Black will hold the opposition.) **3...Ka4 4.Bc3!!** (The final point. It's *zugzwang*.) **4...Rxc3 5.Kxc3** and White has a winning King and pawn ending.

394) 1.Bh3+ Kd6 (1...Kf6 2.Bd7 and 3.e8=Q wins.) **2.Bd7!! Kxd7 3.e8=Q+ Kxe8 4.Rxh8+** and **5.Rxb8** next wins.

395) 1.Ne7! Amazingly powerful. Now Black's Rook gets forked no matter where it runs: 1...Rb6(f6.) then 2.Nd5+; 1...Rd6(h6.) 2.Nf5+; 1...Rg7 2.Nf5+.) **1...Rg3 2.Nf5+ Kf4 3.Nxg3 Kxg3 4.h5** and the pawn can't be caught.

396) 1.Rg3! Be4 (1...Bc6 2.Rc3 Bd7 3.Rb3! Kg8 4.Rb8+ Kh7 5.Rb7, or 1...Be2 2.Rg2! wins. Also on 1...Bh5 2.Rh3 Bf7 3.Rh8+ Bg8 4.Kg6 wins.) **2.Re3 Bh7** (2...Bg2 3.Re2 Bf3 [3...Bf1 4.Rf2] 4.Rf2! Be4 5.Ke5+ wins.) **3.Rb3! Ke8 4.Rb8+ Kd7 5.Rb7+** wins.

397) 1.Rg8 Kd7 2.Rh8! Kd8 3.Ke6 and the Bishop is lost.

398) 1.Kf5! (Threatening 2.Kg6 and 3.Ra8.) **1...Kg8 2.Ra4! Be1** (2...Be7 3.Kg6 and 4.Ra8 wins; or 2...Bf2 3.Kg6 Kf8 4.Rf4+; or 2...Bd8 3.Ra8.) **3.Kg6 Kf8 4.Rf4+! Kg8** (4...Ke8 5.Re4+ and 6.Rxe1.) **5.Re4** and the threats of 6.Re8# and 6.Rxe1 can't be defended.

399) 1.Rd4! (*Zugzwang*.) **1...Bf1** (Or 1...Bg2 2.Rg4+; if 1...Bc8 2.Rd8+.) **2.Kg6 Kf8 3.Rf4+** and 4.Rxf1 wins.

400) 1.Rf5! (Not 1.Rf4? Ba3! 2.Rxc4 Kf8! drawing as the King can head for the "safe" corner [opposite-colored to the Bishop] at a8 and it's a theoretical draw. This is because if the White King and Rook approach too close it will be stalemate. For example: With the Black King at a8, the Bishop at b8 and, say, the White King at b6 and the Rook at h6, the pinning Rh8 would stalemate.) **1...Bc3** (1...c3 2.Rb5! c2 3.Rb8+ Bf8 4.Rc8 c1=Q 5.Rxc1 followed by 6.Rc8 wins.) **2.Rf7!** (*Zugzwang*.) **2...Bb4 3.Rb7 Bd6 4.Rd7 Bf8 5.Rd8 c3 6.Rc8 c2 7.Rxc2** and 8.Rc8 will win.

401) 1.Re1 Ka7 (Or 1...Ba3 2.Rb1+ Kc8 3.Ra1 wins the Bishop since if it moves then 4.Ra8+.) **2.Rf1! Bb4 3.Ra1+ Kb8 4.Rb1** pinning and winning the Bishop.

402) 1...f2! 2.Rf8 Bf3 3.Re8+ Kd2 4.Rd8+ Kc2 5.Rc8+ Kb2 6.Rb8+ Ka2 winning since 7.Ra8+ loses the Rook.

403) 1.e7 Ra2 (1...Ra3 2.Bf2+ and 3.e8=Q.) **2.Kf4 Re2 3.Bf2+!!** (A brilliant diversionary move.) **3...Rxf2+** (If the Black King moves instead, White wins immediately with 4.Be3.) **4.Ke3 Rf1 5.Ke2** and the pawn Queens.

404) 1.Bb4! (Controlling a3 and threatening 2.a7.) **1...Re3** (1...Rd1 2.a7 Ra1 3.Bc3+ wins.) **2.a7 Kf6+ 3.Kf8** (Not 3.Kd8 Kf7! drawing since 4.a8=Q is met by 4...Re8+ and 5...Rxa8.) **3...Rh3 4.Bc3+!** winning since now h8 is controlled.

405) 1.h7 Rb2+! (Best. On 1...Rb8 2.Bb3+! King anywhere 3.Bg8! Rb2+ 4.Kg3 and 5.h8=Q wins.) **2.Kg1** (2.Kh1 also wins.) **2...Rb1+ 3.Bd1! Rxd1+** (3...Rb8 4.Bb3+! King moves 5.Bg8 Rb1+ 6.Kg2 Rb2+ 7.Kg3 and 8.h8=Q wins.) **4.Kg2 Rd2+ 5.Kg3 Rd3+ 6.Kg4 Rd4+ 7.Kg5** and the pawn Queens.

406) 1.d7 Rh8 2.Be8! Rh1+ 3.Ke2 Rh2+ 4.Ke3! (4.Kd3 Rh1 and 5.d8=Q is met by 5...Rd1+.) **4...Rh3+ 5.Ke4 Rh4+ 6.Ke5** and 7.d8=Q winning.

407) 1.Bd5! Re8 (Or 1...Rd8+ 2.Kc7 Re8 3.Bf7 Ra8 4.Be6+ King moves 5.Bc8 Ra7+ 6.Bb7 and 7.g8=Q.) **2.Kd7 Rb8 3.Kc7 Re8 4.Bf7 Ra8 5.Be6+ Kg5 6.Bc8 Ra7+ 7.Bb7** and 8.g8=Q winning.

408) 1.Ke6! (Not 1.Kxc6 Rxg7 2.Bd7 Rg8 and Black can draw.) **1...Rxg7** (1...Rxc8 2.Kd7 Rg8 3.c8=Q Rxc8 4.Kxc8 and 5.g8=Q wins.) **2.Bd7 Rg8 3.Kf7 Rh8 4.Kg7 Ra8 5.Bxc6+** and 6.Bxa8 wins.

409) 1.a7 Rf5+ (1...Rh8? 2.Bf6+.) **2.Ke2 Re5+** (2...Rf8 3.Bf6+! Kc5 4.Be7+ wins.) **3.Kd2 Re8 4.Bf2+ Ke5 5.Bg3+ Ke6 6.Bb8!** shielding a8 from the Rook and assuring Queening.

410) 1...Ke2 2.Re8+ (Forced.) **2...Be3 3.Rf8 Bc1!** (Not 3...f1=Q+ 4.Rxf1 Kxf1 5.Kxb2 drawing.) **4.Re8+ Kf3 5.Rf8+ Bf4** and the pawn Queens.

411) 1.Be3+ Kb7 2.e7 Rxa3 3.Ba7!! (A wonderful concept. Now 3...Rxa7 allows 4.e8=Q, and 3...Kxa7 loses to 4.Kf4 (or Kd4.) 4...Ra4+ 5.Kf5 Ra5+ 6.Kf6 Ra6+ 7.Kf7 and 8.e8=Q.) **3...Ra1 4.Kf4 Rf1+ 5.Bf2!!** (Another shocker, to lure the Rook to a poor square.) **5...Rxf2+ 6.Ke3 Rf1 7.Ke2** and Queens.

412) 1.Rxf2! Bxf2 2.Kxb2 drawing.

413) 1.Rxe4 Bc2 2.Kh8! (Since 2...Bxe4 is stalemate.) **2...a2 3.Re1 Bb1 4.Re5!!** Incredible!. Now 4...a1=Q stalemates and 4...a1=R is met by 5.Ra5!! as 5...Rxa5 is stalemate. Otherwise White plays 5.Ra5, capturing the pawn next and drawing.

414) 1.b6 Rxe5 2.Bd3! Rh5 (Also losing are 2...Re6 3.Bc4+ or 2...Rd5 3.Bc4+.) **3.Bc4+ Ka3 4.b7 Rh8+ 5.Bg8** wins.

415) 1.Rd3! Bf3+ 2.Ka7 d1=Q 3.Rxd6+!! Qxd6 stalemate.

416) 1.Ba6! (Threatening 2.b8=Q Rxb8 3.Bc8! and 4.d8=Q.) **1...Rb8 2.g8=Q!** (diverting the Rook.) **2...Rxg8 3.b8=Q! Rxb8 4.Bc8!** shielding d8 and Queening next.

417) 1...Rxe5! 2.dxe5 Kxe5 3.a5 Kd5 (Black draws because the Bishop is the wrong color to control the a8 Queening square.) **4.a6 Kc6 5.Kg5 Kc7** ("Threatening" 6...Kb8-a8 with the well-known drawing fortress.) **6.Ba7 Kc6** (Now 7...Kb5 is threatened, winning the pawn.) **7.Bc5 Kc7** and White must allow the draw as Black is once again heading for b8-a8 and 8.Ba7 Kc6 repeats the position.

418) 1.Rb6! (Forcing Black's King back, which allows White's King to advance.) **1...Kd7 2.Kd5 Bg3 3.Rb7+ Bc7 4.Ra7!** (It's *zugzwang* again.) **4...Kd8 5.Kc6 Bg3 6.d5 Be5 7.d6** and Black can safely resign.

419) White can make no progress. If the Rook moves off the 6th rank, then the Bishop takes the pawn with check (If it weren't check, then the Rook could return to g6, pinning and winning the Bishop). If the White King moves then again ...Bxd6 draws immediately.

420) 1.Kf4! Bxg4 (1...Bc8 2.Rb8 wins due to the threat of 3.Rh8+; the same holds true for 1...Bd7 2.Rb7 with 3.Rh7+.) **2.Rb8 Kh5** (2...Bh5 3.Rh8 followed by 4.Rxh5+.) **3.Rh8+** winning the Bishop.

421) 1.e7! Kf7 (White threatened 2.Ke6.) **2.Rd7! Bc5 3.e8=Q+! Kxe8 4.Ke6 Be3** (4...Bb6 5.Rb7 Bd8 6.Rb8 wins, 4...Bg1 5.Rg7 wins as does 4...Bf2 5.Rd2 Be3 6.Re2 leaving the Bishop "in hock", e.g., 6...Bh6 7.Rh2 Bg7 8.Ra2! Kd8 9.Ra8+ Kc7 10.Ra7+ and 11.Rxg7, while 6...Bd4 7.Kd5+ and 6...Bf4 7.Kf5+ wins; other squares allow decisive entry of the Rook to the 8th rank: 6...Bc5 7.Rc2 Be7 8.Rc8+ Bd8 9.Rb8.) **5.Rd3 Bf2 6.Rd2** and White wins as in the last note.

422) 1...Bg6! (Since 2.Kxg6 stalemates.) **2.Rf1 Bxf7** with a theoretically drawn Bishop vs Rook ending.

423) 1.Rd6+ Kg7 2.g6 Kh6 (To stop 3.Kg6 and 4.Rd7+.) **3.Kf5** (With the idea of 4.Kf6.) **3...Kg7 4.Rd7+ Kf8 5.Kf6 Ke8 6.g7** winning.

424) 1.Rg7+! Kxh6 (1...Kh8 2.Kg6 is hopeless.) **2.Rg6+ Kh7** (2...Kh5 3.Rg3! wins.) **3.Kf6 Bd4+ 4.Kf7 Ba7** (Or 4...Bc5 5.Rg5 and 6.Rh5+.) **5.Ra6! Bb8 6.Rb6! Bc7** (6...Ba7 7.Rb7 wins.) **7.Rb7! Be5** (7...Bd8 8.Ke8+ or 7...Bd6 8.Ke6+ wins.) **8.Rb5** and 9.Rh5+. Other moves lose in a similar fashion.

425) 1.h6! (Not 1.Re8+ Bg8 "threatening" stalemate.) **1...Ba2 2.h7 Bf7+** (Hoping for 3.Rxf7?? stalemate.) **3.Kxf7** winning.

426) 1...Bd3! (Stopping h7 and Kh6, which would win.) **2.h7** (2.Kf6 Bc4 3.Ra8+ Bg8 draws- note 4.Kg6 stalemates.) **2...Bxh7 3.Ra8+ Bg8** and it's a theoretical draw as Black's King is in a "good" corner (i.e., of opposite color to the Bishop.), for example 3.Ra8+ Bg8 is an airtight fortress since 4.Kg6 (or f6 or h6.) stalemates.

427) 1.Rd8+ Bf8 2.Rb8 b5 (Forced.) **3.Rxb5 Bd6 4.Rd5 Be7 5.Ra5 Bd6 6.Ra8+ Bf8 7.Rb8** and mate next.

428) 1.Ke3! (The Rook can't leave g1 since the pawn needs protection.) **1...Kf1 2.Be2+** (Not 2.Kd4 Kf2.) **2...Ke1 3.Bf3 Kf1 4.Be2+** drawing by repetition.

429) 1.Bd5!! Rh5 (1...cxd5 [now the pawn "interferes" with the Rook's lateral mobility- i.e., Rb5 isn't possible] 2.Kf7 Rf5+ 3.Ke7 Re5+ 4.Kd7 and 5.b8=Q, or 1...Rxd5 ["attracting" the Rook to d5 since now after 2.b8=Q, the move ...Rg8+ is not available] 2.b8=Q.) **2.Kf8 cxd5** (2...Rh8+ 3.Bg8 and 4.b8=Q.) **3.Kg7 Rg5+ 4.Kf7 Rf5+ 5.Ke7 Re5+ 6.Kd7** winning.

430) 1...Rd6+!! drawing as 2.Kxd6 or Bxd6 stalemate, and other King moves allow 2...Rxe6 winning both pawns. 1...Rxd7!! also draws, as 2.exd7 stalemates!

431) 1.Bf2! (Not 1.d7? Rd6+!) **1...Ke8 2.Bh4 Rc3+ 3.Kd5 Rd3+ 4.Kc5 Rd2** (4...Rc3+ 5.Kd4 and 6.d7+ wins.) **5.Bg5!** (So that if 5...Rd1 then 6.Kc6 wins as 6...Rc1+ isn't possible.) **5...Rd3 6.Kc6 Rc3+ 7.Kd5 Rd3+ 8.Kc5! Rd1** (8...Rc3+ 9.Kd4 and 10.d7+.) **9.Kc6** and 10.d7+ wins.

432) 1...Rf2 (Waiting.) **2.Be5** (2.Bh6+ Kg8 3.Ke5 Re2+ 4.Kd6 Rf2 5.Ke7 Re2+ gets White nowhere.) **2...Rf1** (Waiting.) **3.Kd5 Rf2 4.Ke6 Rf3!** **5.f7** (5.g7+ Kg8 and the light-squared blockade is airtight.) **5...Rf6+!** drawing since 6.Kxf6 or 6.Bxf6 stalemates, and 7.Kd7(or Kd5.) 7...Rxg6 and 8...Kxf7 also draws.

QUEEN ENDINGS

Endgames involving the Queen have rightly earned a reputation for extreme complexity, due in part to the seemingly endless number of checks available. Yet these endings do obey an inner logic, and the student is advised to study their underlying patterns–the variations will take care of themselves.

Included in this chapter are the basic endings with Queen vs pawn(s) on the sixth and seventh rank and the zigzag winning method every chessplayer *must know*. These endings occur over and over again in practice and although they are few in number, a knowledge of them will pay great dividends. In Queen and pawn endings it is also important to remember that having the *most advanced passed pawn* is normally more important than having a material superiority. The materially weaker side in Queen endings must also be constantly on the lookout for the possibility of perpetual check as a drawing method.

W   + -

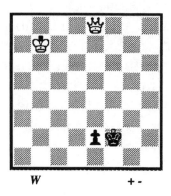

W   + -

B   =

No.433
HINT: A center pawn almost always loses against the enemy King and Queen, even if the pawn is on the 7th rank (2nd for Black) and its King is right next to it. White wins by zig-zag checks with the Queen to force the Black King to block his pawn, then the White King can inch forward to cooperate with the Queen to mate.

EASY

No.434
HINT: White's King and Queen are more distant from the enemy center pawn than in the previous example, but nonetheless similar zig-zag Queen maneuvers combined with the approach of the White King are decisive; i.e., the distance of the King and Queen does not help Black's defense at all.

EASY

No.435
HINT: Although a center pawn almost always loses to the combined efforts of the enemy King and Queen, here we have an exceptional case worth remembering. The position of the White King on the d-file shields the Black King from the deadly zig-zag checking of the White Queen, and so Black draws in a straightforward manner.

EASY

B   **=**

No.436
HINT: With the c- or f-pawn on the 7th rank (2nd for Black) and its King nearby, the game is almost always drawn because of a stalemate defense.

EASY

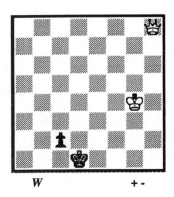

W   **+ -**

No.437
HINT: With the move White can maneuver his Queen to keep the Black King from running toward a1 (Which allows a stalemate defense we saw in the previous example.) then the White King can approach decisively to force mate.

MODERATE

B   **=**

No.438
HINT: An a- or h-pawn on the 7th rank (2nd for Black) rank with its King nearby almost always draws; the key motif for the defense is stalemate.

EASY

W + -

No.439

HINT: The White King approaches while blocking the White Queen's action down the g-file, thus neutralizing Black's stalemate defenses. Eventually White even allows Black to promote the h-pawn, but a fine move of the White King follows, leaving Black unable to stop mate.

DIFFICULT

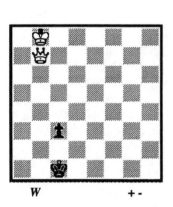

W + -

No.440

HINT: A c-pawn or f-pawn on the 6th rank (3rd for Black) almost always loses. The defender's main problem is the lack of a stalemate resource as the enemy Queen closes in.

MODERATE

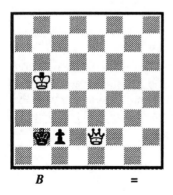

B =

No.441

HINT: Black draws by initially using a stalemate defense; then when the White King moves in to try to force a mate, Black narrowly avoids disaster because his newly created Queen will be attacking the White Queen, buying a vital tempo to ward off the mating net.

MODERATE

W   + -

No.442

HINT: Paradoxically, having more than one pawn against a Queen usually is a disadvantage for the defender. This is because the extra pawn typically disallows stalemate defenses, as the extra pawn will normally be able to move. Here White takes advantage of this fact to move in with King and Queen to effect mate.

EASY

B   =

No.443

HINT: Though the extra Black pawn would normally work in White's favor (Because it rules out stalemate defenses.), here Black can draw because the White King is too far away and the a-pawn can be used to decoy the White Queen at the right moment, reducing the position to the standard theoretical draw seen in earlier examples.

EASY

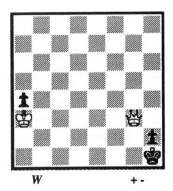

W   + -

No.444

HINT: White uses Black's a-pawn against him by forcing Black to move it, which allows the White Queen to work in to force mate by herself.

MODERATE

B   =

No.445

HINT: Black, who is in check, has only one correct drawing move. The wrong one loses a pawn and leaves Black with just one center pawn, which (As we know from some early examples of this chapter.) is a theoretically lost position.

EASY

W   + -

No.446

HINT: With the White King nearby White normally wins against two connected pawns on the 7th rank; White's Queen deftly attacks both the Black King and the pawns, eventually winning one of them. Then the remaining single center pawn loses, as the earliest examples of this chapter demonstrated.

EASY

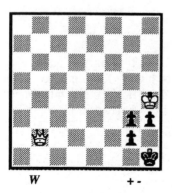

W   + -

No.447

HINT: This position involves tricky tactics by both players. The White Queen uses pinning as well as timely waiting moves to shut down Black's resistance.

DIFFICULT

W   + -

No.448

HINT: In almost all cases Queen vs. Queen endings will be drawn. Except sometimes there can be surprising tactical twists which force the win. From this position, by using zig-zag checks, the White Queen gradually approaches the vicinity of the Black King to force mate.

MODERATE

W   + -

No.449

HINT: White's first move is critical. The wrong check with the White Queen allows Black to draw; the right check mates in a few moves.

MODERATE

W   + -

No.450

HINT: White is in check and it might seem he has no hope of winning. Yet the right move forces mate in four!

MODERATE

B =

No.451

HINT: A very instructive position in which one Queen will hold off two Queens! After a preliminary check, Black will allow the g-pawn to Queen, but then arranges to force perpetual check.

DIFFICULT

SOLUTIONS FOR EXAMPLES 433-451

433) 1.Qf4+ Kg2 2.Qe3 Kf1 3.Qf3+ (Forcing the Black King to block his pawn.) **3...Ke1 4.Kc5** (Now the White King inches forward.) **4...Kd2 5.Qf4+ Kd1 6.Qd4+ Kc2 7.Qe3 Kd1 8.Qd3+** (Again forcing the Black King in front of the pawn.) **8...Ke1 9.Kd4 Kf2 10.Qe3+ Kf1 11.Qf3+ Ke1 12.Kd3 Kd1 13.Qxe2+** and mate next.

434) 1.Qf7+ Kg2 2.Qe6 Kf2 3.Qf5+ (The Queen zig-zags forward to force the Black King to eventually block his own pawn.) **3...Kg2 4.Qe4+ Kf2 5.Qf4+ Kg2 6.Qe3 Kf1 7.Qf3+ Ke1 8.Kc6** (Now the White King can move up to help the Queen.) **8...Kd2 9.Qf2 Kd1 10.Qd4+ Kc2 11.Qe3 Kd1 12.Qd3+** (The process is repeated, allowing the White King to come still closer.) **12...Ke1 13.Kd5 Kf2 14.Qd2 Kf1 15.Qf4+ Kg2 16.Qe3 Kf1 17.Qf3+ Ke1 18.Kd4 Kd2 19.Qf2 Kd1 20.Kd3! e1=Q 21.Qc2#.**

435) 1...e2 2.Kc4 (A feeble hope–if Black decided to mock White by playing 2...Kd1?? expecting that 3...e1=Q cannot be stopped, then he would be rudely awakened by 3.Qd7+ and White wins by the familiar zig-zag checking pattern of the previous examples.) **2...e1=Q.** No such luck! It's a dead draw.

436) 1...Ka1! (The right way, as now 2.Qxc2 is stalemate; but not 1...Kc1? as then 2.Ke3 wins, after 2...Kd1 3.Kd3.) **2.Qc3+ Kb1 3.Qd3 Ka1 4.Qd2 Kb1** and White is getting nowhere.

437) 1.Qd4+ Kc1 (1...Ke1 2.Kf3! c1=Q 3.Qf2+ Kd1 4.Qe2#.) **2.Qb4!** (Keeping the Black King from running to b1 and, subsequently, to a1–which would allow the standard stalemate defense seen in the previous example.) **2...Kd1 3.Qb3 Kd2 4.Qb2 Kd1** (On 4...Kd3 5.Qc1 is decisive.) **5.Kf3 Kd2** (5...c1=Q 6.Qe2#.) **6.Ke4 Kd1 7.Kd3! c1=Q 8.Qe2#.**

438) 1...h2 2.Qg3+ Kh1 (Now the White Queen must move as otherwise it's stalemate.) **3.Qe1+ Kg2 4.Qe2+ Kg1** (Now 4...Kh1?? allows 5.Qf1#; also 4...Kh3? 5.Qf1+ controls the key h1-square, with a win for White.) **5.Qg4+ Kh1** and White can make no progress.

439) 1.Kg6! (Shielding the g-file to stop stalemate.) **1...Kg2 2.Kf5+ Kf2** (Or 2...Kh1 3.Kg4! Kg2 4.Qb7+ Kg1 5.Kg3! h1=Q 6.Qb1#.) **3.Qd4+ Kg2 4.Qd2+ Kg1** (4...Kg3 5.Qd5 and 6.Qh1.) **5.Kf4!! h1=Q 6.Kg3! Qe4 7.Qd1+ Qe1+ 8.Qxe1#.**

440) 1.Qh1+ Kb2 2.Qh8! (This pin holds up the advance of the pawn to the 7th rank.) **2...Kb3** (On 2...Kc2 3.Qd4 keeps Black in a bind.) **3.Qd4 c2** (3...Kb2 4.Kb7, and the White King approaches with decisive result.) **4.Qa1 Kc4 5.Qc1** and with the pawn securely blockaded, the White King strolls forward for a simple win.

441) 1...Ka1! (As 2.Qxc2 stalemates; but 3...Kb1? loses after 4.Kb4! c1=Q 5.Kb3 and mate cannot be stopped.) **2.Qd2 Kb1 3.Kb4** (Trying a mating scheme similar to the one of the previous note, but with the White Queen now on d2 Black can defend.) **3...c1=Q** and it's a draw since White has no time for Kb3, as now the White Queen is attacked by the new Black Queen.

442) 1.Qg4+ Kh1 2.Qh3+ Kg1 3.Qg3+ Kf1 (On 3...Kh1 White simply snatches the f-pawn as there is no stalemate due to the presence of the h-pawn.) **4.Kc4 Ke1 5.Kd3 Kf1 6.Kd2 h5 7.Qh2 h4 8.Qh1#.**

443) 1...Kf1 (Not 1...Kh1 as 2.Qxf2 is not stalemate because of the a-pawn's presence.) **2.Kb7** (The White King rushes in.) **2...a4 3.Kc6 a3** (Just in time the a-pawn diverts the White Queen–before the White King can approach too close–and forces a reduction into a standard draw with the f-pawn.) **4.Qxa3 Kg2 5.Qb2 Kh1** and Black draws easily as now 6.Qxf2 really is stalemate and the White King is still too far away to help out.

444) 1.Kb4! (White releases the a-pawn to prevent stalemate; this also allows the White Queen to move in for the kill.) **1...a3 2.Qf2 a2 3.Qf1#.**

445) 1...Ke4 (The only way; after 1...Kd4? 2.Qf4+ Kd3 3.Qf3+ and 4.Qxe2 Black loses.) **2.Qg4+ Ke3 3.Qe6+ Kf2 4.Qf6+ Ke1** (Not 4...Ke3 because of 5.Qc3+ and 6.Qxd2.) **5.Qh4+ Kd1 6.Qg4 Kc1 7.Qc4+ Kd1** and Black draws easily. White can only run in circles.

446) 1.Qh6+ Kd3 2.Qd6+ Kc3 (Or 2...Ke3 3.Qc5+ Kd3 4.Qc2+ Ke3 5.Qc3+ capturing the d-pawn and winning as in our main line.) **3.Qc5+ Kd3 4.Qc2+ Ke3 5.Qc3+ Kf2 6.Qxd2** and we have an easy theoretical win because Black has a center pawn remaining, which is an easy win for White. (See the first examples in this chapter.)

447) 1.Qb7 (The g-pawn must be pinned.) **1...Kh2** (On 1...h2 2.Qe4! forces mate after 2...Kg1 3.Qe1#.) **2.Qd7! g1=N** (A clever attempt to hold; the obvious 2...g1=Q is blasted by 3.Qxh3#.) **3.Qd6! Ne2 4.Qd2 g2 5.Qxe2 Kh1 6.Qf3!** (Again a pin to limit Black's resources.) **6...h2 7.Qe4!** (A fine finishing move.) **7...Kg1** (There's no other choice.) **8.Qe1#.**

448) 1.Qb7+! Kc1 (After 1...Ka2 2.Kc2!, and suddenly Black has no defense against mate at b3.) **2.Qc6+ Kb2 3.Qb5+ Ka3 4.Qa5+ Kb2 5.Qb4+ Ka2** (Or 5...Kc1 6.Qd2+ Kb1 7.Qc2#.) **6.Kc2!** and Black gets mated.

449) 1.Qc4+! (But not 1.Qa5+ as then 1...Kb1! and White will have no way to force a mating net.) **1...Ka3 2.Qa6+ Kb2 3.Qb5+ Kc1** (On 3...Ka3 4.Qa5+ Kb2 5.Qb4+ Ka2 [if 5...Kc1 then 6.Qd2+ Kb1 7.Qc2#] 6.Kc2! mates; or 3...Ka2 4.Kc2!, again mating.) **4.Qc4+ Kb2** (4...Kd1 5.Qc2+ Ke1 6.Qe2#.) **5.Qb4+ Ka2 6.Kc2!** and mate is forced.

450) 1.Kg3+ Kg1 2.Qa7+! Kh1 3.Qh7+ Kg1 4.Qh2#.

451) 1...Qh4+ 2.Qh7 (After 2.Kg8 Qd8+ 3.Kf7 Qd7+ 4.Kf6 Qd4+! 5.Kg6 Qg4+ White can't make any progress as the Black Queen "follows" the White King everywhere with harassing checks.) **2...Qd8+!** (A brilliant concept– Black encourages White to promote the g-pawn.) **3.g8=Q Qf6+ 4.Qgg7** (Or 4.Qhg7 Qh4+ 5.Q8h7 Qd8+ and, as in our main line, the two Queens cannot stop Black's lone Queen from the perpetual checking.) **4...Qd8+ 5.Qhg8 Qh4+ 6.Q7h7 Qf6+,** etc. White must acquiesce to the draw a full Queen ahead!